101 best campsites

for walking & cycling

2013 Edition

alan rogers

Compiled by: **Alan Rogers Guides Ltd**

Designed by: **Vine Design Ltd**

© Alan Rogers Guides Ltd 2012

Published by: **Alan Rogers Guides Ltd,**
Spelmonden Old Oast, Goudhurst, Kent TN17 1HE

www.alanrogers.com
Tel: 01580 214000

British Library Cataloguing-in-Publication Data:
A catalogue record for this book is available from
the British Library.

ISBN 978-1-909057-01-2

Printed in Great Britain by
Stephens & George Print Group

contents

Welcome to the Alan Rogers
'101' **guides**

The Alan Rogers guides have been helping campers and caravanners make informed decisions about their holiday destinations since 1968. Today, whether online or in print, Alan Rogers still provides an independent, impartial view, with detailed reports, on each campsite.

With so much unfiltered, unqualified information freely available, the Alan Rogers perspective is invaluable to make sure you make the right choice for your holiday.

What is the '101' **series**?

At Alan Rogers, we know that readers have many and diverse interests, hobbies and particular requirements. And we know that our guides, featuring a total of some 3,000 campsites, can provide a bewildering choice from which it can be difficult to produce a shortlist of possible holiday destinations.

The Alan Rogers 101 guides are devised as a means of presenting a realistic, digestible number of great campsites, featured because of their suitability to a given theme.

This book remains first and foremost an authoritative guide to excellent campsites you should consider when looking for a camping holiday with plenty of scope for walking and/or cycling opportunities for a range of levels.

101 **Best campsites for walking and cycling**

Among the most popular activities while camping are walking and cycling. It's not surprising when so many campsites are set amid glorious scenery and beautiful countryside.

This guide highlights 101 campsites which are all worth considering and short listing for your holiday walking or cycling excursions. All offer scenic routes, often directly from the campsite's own gates. Some are located right on official way marked paths or trails – an indication that you are certain to find some wonderful itineraries and lovely countryside.

Of course much depends on what kind of level you are expecting or wanting. Those looking for a rigorous daily workout and some serious exercise will have differing needs to those who fancy a little off-site exploration under their own steam while staying on the campsite.

One thing that is constant is the sense of quiet satisfaction that follows an excursion, however challenging, whether on wheels or on foot. After a leisurely ramble or a hard morning's pedal pushing, you return tired but having enjoyed new perspectives, and with a small sense of accomplishment.

Alan Rogers – in search
of 'the best'

Alan Rogers himself started off with the very specific aim of providing people with the necessary information to allow them to make an informed decision about their holiday destination. Today we still do that with a range of guides that now covers Europe's best campsites in 27 countries.

We work with campsites all day, every day. We visit campsites for inspection purposes (or even just for pleasure!). We know campsites 'inside out'.

We know which campsites would suit active families; which are great for get-away-from-it-all couples; we know which campsites are planning super new pool complexes; which campsites offer a fantastic menu in their on-site restaurant; which campsites allow you to launch a small boat from their slipway; which campsites have a decent playing area for kicking a ball around; which campsites have flat, grassy pitches and which have solid hard standings.

We also know which are good for fishing, golf, spas, children, nature and outdoor activities; which are close to the beach; and which welcome dogs. These particular themes form our '101' series.

All Alan Rogers guides (and our website) are respected for their independent, impartial and honest assessment. The reviews are prose-based, without overuse of indecipherable icons and symbols. Our simple aim is to help guide you to a campsite that matches best your requirements – often quite difficult in today's age of information overload.

What is the **best**?

The criteria we use when inspecting and selecting sites are numerous, but the most important by far is the question of good quality. People want different things from their choice of campsite, so campsite 'styles' vary dramatically: from small peaceful campsites in the heart of the countryside, to 'all singing, all dancing' sites in popular seaside resorts.

The size of the site, whether it's part of a chain or privately owned, makes no difference in terms of it being required to meet our exacting standards in respect of its quality and it being 'fit for purpose'. In other words, irrespective of the size of the site, or the number of facilities it offers, we consider and evaluate the welcome, the pitches, the sanitary facilities, the cleanliness, the general maintenance and even the location.

Expert opinions

We rely on our dedicated team of Site Assessors, all of whom are experienced campers, caravanners or motorcaravanners, to visit and recommend campsites. Each year they travel around Europe inspecting new campsites for Alan Rogers and re-inspecting the existing ones.

When planning
your **holiday...**

A holiday should always be a relaxing affair, and a campsite-based holiday particularly so. Our aim is for you to find the ideal campsite for your holiday, one that suits your requirements. All Alan Rogers guides provide a wealth of information, including some details supplied by campsite owners themselves, and the following points may help ensure that you plan a successful holiday.

Find out more

An Alan Rogers reference number (**eg FR 12345**) is given for each campsite and can be useful for finding more information and pictures online at **www.alanrogers.com**

Simply enter this number in the 'Campsite Search' field on the Home page.

Campsite descriptions

We aim to convey an idea of its general appearance, 'feel' and features, with details of pitch numbers, electricity, hardstandings etc.

Facilities

We list specific information on the site's facilities and amenities and, where available, the dates when these facilities are open (if not for the whole season). Much of this information is as supplied to us and may be subject to change. Should any particular activity or aspect of the campsite be important to you, it is always worth discussing with the campsite before you travel.

Swimming pools

Opening dates, any charges and levels of supervision are provided where we have been notified. In some countries (notably France) there is a regulation whereby Bermuda-style shorts may not be worn in swimming pools (for health and hygiene reasons). It is worth ensuring that you do take 'proper' swimming trunks with you.

Charges

Those given are the latest provided to us, usually 2012 prices, and should be viewed as a guide only.

Toilet blocks

We assume that toilet blocks will be equipped with a reasonable number of British style WCs, washbasins and hot showers in cubicles. We also assume that there will be an identified chemical toilet disposal point, and that the campsite will provide water and waste water drainage points and bin areas. If not the case, we comment. We do mention certain features that some readers find important: washbasins in cubicles, facilities for babies, facilities for those with disabilities and motorcaravan service points.

Reservations

Necessary for high season (roughly mid-July to mid-August) in popular holiday areas (i.e. beach resorts). You can reserve many sites via our own Alan Rogers Travel Service or through other tour operators. Remember, many sites are closed all winter and you may struggle to get an answer.

Telephone numbers

All numbers assume that you are phoning from within the country in question. From the UK or Ireland, dial 00, then the country's prefix (e.g. France is 33), then the campsite number given, but dropping the first '0'.

Opening dates

Dates given are those provided to us and can alter before the start of the season. If you intend to visit shortly after a published opening date, or shortly before the closing date, it is wise to check that it will actually be open at the time required. Similarly some sites operate a restricted service during the low season, only opening some of their facilities (e.g. swimming pools) during the main season; where we know about this, and have the relevant dates, we indicate it – again if you are at all doubtful it is wise to check.

Accommodation

Over recent years, more and more campsites have added high quality mobile homes, chalets, lodges, gites and more. Where applicable we indicate what is available and you'll find details online.

Special Offers

Some campsites have taken the opportunity to highlight a special offer. This is arranged by them and for clarification please contact the campsite direct.

Two **legs good**,
two **wheels good**

It's all part of the enduring appeal of camping: a relaxed way of life, lungfuls of clear, fresh air and beautiful countryside to explore. And how better to do so than on foot or on wheels. Whether you're looking for serious exercise or just want to get to know your surroundings, walking and cycling are a great solution.

Get **walking and cycling**

Walking and hiking are ever popular activities, being environmentally friendly and convenient. Cycle hire is often available (handy for collecting bread as well as exploring some beauty spots) and some campsites endeavour to make the most of their surroundings with marked trails.

Many campsites across Europe have invested heavily in impressive infrastructure and state of the art facilities. But simple enjoyment of the outdoor environment and a little curiosity about one's surroundings is all that is required to enjoy some walking and cycling while on holiday.
And if it prises the children away from the computer screen for a while then so much the better!

Why **do it?**

Shape up!
Even on holiday, some people want to stay in trim. Others simply enjoy a little gentle exercise each day.

A unique viewpoint
When you're moving through the countryside under your own power, you have every chance to stop whenever you like. In a car the landscape flashes past, you don't see the details and you can't pause to savour something that catches your eye.

Small challenges
Enjoy that feeling of quiet satisfaction when you return from a challenging ride or a walk through the local forest, with only your pioneer map reading skills to bring you back to civilisation.

Learn about your natural surroundings
You're on holiday, your surroundings are unfamiliar; why not get out and explore? Enjoy getting to know the local flora and fauna.

It's free!
Apart from any special kit or hire charges, you can enjoy time with the family without paying handsomely for commercial attractions and the like.
You'll also save on fuel costs.

On two **legs**

Walking is perhaps the simplest means of deriving pleasure while on holiday. It doesn't have to be strenuous - a walk through the adjacent meadows or into the village for an evening meal allows you to become a small part of local life for a while. And it's good for you too!

Walking **the walk**

Being usually rurally located, you'll find many sites are geared up to encourage walkers. Some will even have walking notes and maps in reception for you to borrow and leaflets to help you spot local wildlife. Some take it to another level by organising accompanied rambles or hikes – these are generally excellent, giving you the chance to discover the best of the locality with the first-hand knowledge of a local.

Serious all-weather hikers might like to know which sites have special drying rooms for wet clothing and boots and which can provide packed lunches.

Walking **to suit you**

Explore the area

Very often campsites are bordered by fields, forest, seafront or even some kind of protected national park, so you'll often find paths that allow you to explore the neighbourhood.

Walking with a purpose

Many campsites are wonderfully located close to a magnificent chateau, a famous bridge, a stunning local view... Others are set just outside a village where a decent stroll takes you to local restaurants without the old debate of whose turn it is to drive.

Walking to wake up!

On a campsite it's always a pleasure to feel virtuous and walk to fetch the morning bread from the campsite shop, even on the largest sites, when you are pitched at the farthest point. It's part of the morning ritual and a pleasant start to the day, not a chore. It's about doing something a little different from the usual routine at home.

Walking **for health**

Walking is an ideal exercise for maintaining health and fitness – it's low impact, low cost and requires no training!

On
two **wheels**

Cycling is an activity all the family can take part in. Bikes loaded on the back of a 'van or roof of a car are a common site on the motorways across Europe during summer months. With bikes on board, there's always somewhere to go and a family outing was never more fun.

Cycling **made easy**

Many sites offer a cycle hire service – often with a good range of well maintained bikes, of various sizes and with all the usual accessories. For some the expectation is only for occasional use – a potter around the local village, or an afternoon or two for the youngsters to cycle around the campsite. Elsewhere the approach is more serious, with some serious kit to suit different types of cycling, detailed route notes and guided tours of local itineraries.

Cycling **to suit you**

Mountain biking

The more challenging the terrain, the more likely this is going to be on offer – some sites in the rockier parts of the UK, Alps, Dolomites or Pyrénées offer some world-class terrain for the experienced mountain biker.

Road cycling

Outside the UK, road cyclists are treated with much more consideration and many competitive cyclists do head to the continent with the intention of some serious practice while on holiday. In fact, for some, the camping holiday is merely the means to the end.

Easy going trails

Possibly the largest group, recreational cyclists generally are after an easy going itinerary – it's gentle exercise rather than a punishing regime. They usually bike for the scenery and their bike rides are destination rides. They might spend a Saturday morning biking into the hills to see the autumn foliage, or cycling to a small craft fair to look around or pedalling along the trails in the local forest.

Cycling **for health**

- An easy way to exercise
- Builds strength and muscle tone
- Improves stamina and general fitness
- Good for cardio-vascular fitness
- Helps weight loss
- Reduces stress

You
never **know**

Taking bikes and a pair of decent walking boots on a camping holiday will never be a bad idea. Even if you do not consider yourself a proper 'walker' you never know when you will be confronted by a once-in-a-lifetime spectacular view that cannot be ignored and yet which requires a bit of legwork to get to.

Equally, you might at any time come across an amazing bike trail, leading through superb scenery and crying out to be followed. The opportunities for enjoying some walking and cycling are all around you – don't miss out!

Enjoy...!

Whether you're an 'old hand' or are contemplating your first trip, a regular reader of our Guides or a new 'convert', we wish you well in your travels and hope we have been able to help in some way. We are, of course, also out and about ourselves, visiting sites, talking to owners and readers, and generally checking on standards and new developments. We hope to bump into you!

Wishing you thoroughly enjoyable camping and caravanning in 2013 – favoured by good weather of course!

The Alan Rogers Team

Camping Picos de Europa

E-33556 Avin-Onis (Asturias)
t: 985 844 070 e: adrian@picos-europa.com
alanrogers.com/ES89650 www.picos-europa.com

Accommodation: ☑Pitch ☑Mobile home/chalet ☐ Hotel/B&B ☑ Apartment

This delightful site is, as its name suggests, an ideal spot from which to explore these dramatic limestone mountains on foot, by bicycle or on horseback. The site itself is continuously developing and the dynamic owner, José, and his nephew who helps out when he is away, are both very pleasant and nothing is too much trouble. The site is in a valley beside a pleasant, fast flowing river. The 160 marked pitches are of varying sizes and have been developed in three avenues, on level grass mostly backing on to hedging, with 6A electricity. An area for tents and apartments is over a bridge past the fairly small, but pleasant, round swimming pool. Local stone has been used for the L-shaped building at the main entrance which houses reception and a very good bar/restaurant. The site can organise caving activities, and has information about the Cares gorge along with the many energetic ways of exploring the area, including by canoe and quad-bike! The Bulnes funicular railway is well worth a visit.

You might like to know

The campsite's reception is a mine of useful information about great hiking and mountain biking itineraries, with a good range of maps, books and personal experience!

☑ Walking notes or maps available
☐ Waymarked footpath – direct access from site
☑ Waymarked footpath within 1 km. of site
☐ Cycle trail – direct access from site
☑ Cycle trail access within 2 km. of site
☐ Mountain bike track within 2 km. of site
☐ Bicycle hire on site
☐ Accompanied hiking trips
☐ Accompanied cycling trips
☐ Drying room for wet clothes/boots
☐ Packed lunch service

Facilities: Toilet facilities include a new fully equipped block, along with new facilities for disabled visitors and babies. Pleasant room with tables and chairs for poor weather. Washing machine and dryer. Shop (July-Sept). Swimming pool (Feb-Sept). Bar and cafeteria style restaurant (all year) serves a good value 'menu del dia' and snacks. WiFi in restaurant area (free). Play area. Fishing. Torches necessary in the new tent area. Off site: Riding 12 km. Bicycle hire 15 km. Golf and coast at Llanes 25 km.

Open: All year.

Directions: Avin is 15 km. east of Cangas de Onis on AS114 to Panes and is best approached from this direction especially if towing. From the A8 (Santander-Oviedo) km. 326 exit take N634 northwest to Arriondas. Turn southeast on N625 to Cangas and join AS114 (Covodonga/Panes) bypassing Cangas. Site is beyond Avin after 16 km. marker. GPS: 43.3363, -4.94498

Charges guide

Per unit incl. 2 persons and electricity	€ 20,42 - € 26,06
extra person	€ 5,08 - € 5,40
child (4-14 yrs)	€ 4,05
electricity	€ 3,75

Camping Peña Montañesa

Ctra Ainsa-Francia km 2, E-22360 Labuerda (Huesca)
t: 974 500 032 e: info@penamontanesa.com
alanrogers.com/ES90600 www.penamontanesa.com

Accommodation: ☑Pitch ☑Mobile home/chalet ☐ Hotel/B&B ☐ Apartment

A large site situated quite high up in the Pyrénées near the Ordesa National Park, Peña Montañesa is easily accessible from Ainsa or from France via the Bielsa Tunnel (steep sections on the French side). The site is essentially divided into three sections opening progressively throughout the season and all have shade. The 288 pitches on fairly level grass are of about 75 sq.m. and 10A electricity is available on virtually all. Grouped near the entrance are the facilities that make the site so attractive, including a fair sized outdoor pool and a glass-covered indoor pool with jacuzzi and sauna. Here too is an attractive bar/restaurant with an open fire and a terrace, a supermarket and takeaway are opposite. There is an entertainment programme for children (21/6-15/9 and Easter weekend) and twice weekly for adults in July and August. This is quite a large site which has grown very quickly and as such, it may at times be a little hard pressed, although it is very well run. The site is ideally situated for exploring the beautiful Pyrénées. The complete town of Ainsa is listed as a national monument of Spain and should be explored while you are here, along with the national park.

You might like to know

This site is a great base for many adventure sports including canyoning, potholing and mountain biking.

- ☑ Walking notes or maps available
- ☐ Waymarked footpath – direct access from site
- ☑ Waymarked footpath within 1 km. of site
- ☐ Cycle trail – direct access from site
- ☑ Cycle trail access within 2 km. of site
- ☐ Mountain bike track within 2 km. of site
- ☐ Bicycle hire on site
- ☑ Accompanied hiking trips
- ☑ Accompanied cycling trips
- ☐ Drying room for wet clothes/boots
- ☐ Packed lunch service

Facilities: A newer toilet block, heated when necessary, has free hot showers but cold water to open plan washbasins. Facilities for disabled visitors. Small baby room. An older block in the original area has similar provision. Washing machine and dryer. Bar, restaurant, takeaway and supermarket (all 1/1-31/12). Outdoor swimming pool (1/4-31/10). Indoor pool (all year). Playground. Boules. Bicycle hire. Riding. Rafting. Only gas barbecues are permitted. Torches required in some areas. WiFi (free).
Off site: Fishing 100 m. Skiing in season. Canoeing nearby.

Open: All year.

Directions: Site is 2 km. from Ainsa, on the road from Ainsa to France. GPS: 42.4352, 0.13618

Charges guide

Per unit incl. 2 persons and electricity	€ 25,25 - € 33,70

Camping Boltaña

Ctra N260 km. 442, E-22340 Boltaña (Huesca)
t: **974 502 347** e: info@campingboltana.com
alanrogers.com/ES90620 www.campingboltana.com

Accommodation: ☑Pitch ☑Mobile home/chalet ☐ Hotel/B&B ☐ Apartment

Nestled in the Rio Ara valley, surrounded by the Pyrénées mountains and below a tiny but enchanting, historic, hill top village, is the very pretty, thoughtfully planned Camping Boltaña. Generously sized, 190 grassy pitches (all with 10A electricity) have good shade from a variety of trees and a stream meanders through the campsite. The landscaping includes ten charming rocky water gardens and a covered pergola doubles as an eating and play area. A stone building houses the site's reception, social room and supermarket. Angel Moreno, the owner of the site, is a charming host and has tried to think of everything to make his guests comfortable.

You might like to know

There are some excellent accompanied mountain bike trips into the spectacular Ordesa National Park.

- ☑ Walking notes or maps available
- ☐ Waymarked footpath – direct access from site
- ☑ Waymarked footpath within 1 km. of site
- ☐ Cycle trail – direct access from site
- ☑ Cycle trail access within 2 km. of site
- ☑ Mountain bike track within 2 km. of site
- ☐ Bicycle hire on site
- ☐ Accompanied hiking trips
- ☑ Accompanied cycling trips
- ☐ Drying room for wet clothes/boots
- ☐ Packed lunch service

Facilities: Two modern sanitary blocks include facilities for disabled visitors and laundry facilities. Supermarket. Bar, restaurant and takeaway (1/7-31/8). Swimming pools (15/6-15/9). Playground. Entertainment for children (high season). Pétanque. Guided tours, plus hiking, canyoning, rafting, climbing, mountain biking and caving. Bicycle hire. WiFi. No charcoal barbecues. Torches useful in some parts. Off site: Local bus service. Fishing 1 km.

Open: 15 January - 15 December.

Directions: South of the Park Nacional de Ordesa, site is 50 km. from Jaca near Ainsa. From Ainsa travel northwest on N260 toward Boltaña (near 443 km. marker) and 1 km. from Boltaña turn south toward Margudgued. Site is well signed and is 1 km. along this road. GPS: 42.43018, 0.07882

Charges guide

Per unit incl. 2 persons and electricity	€ 35,40
extra person	€ 6,50
child (1-10 yrs)	€ 5,50
dog	€ 3,25

PORTUGAL – Odemira

Zmar-Eco Camping Resort

Herdade A de Mateus EN393/1, San Salvador, P-7630 Odemira (Beja)
t: 707 200 626 e: info@zmar.eu
alanrogers.com/PO8175 www.zmar.eu

Accommodation: ☑Pitch ☑Mobile home/chalet ☐ Hotel/B&B ☐ Apartment

Zmar is an exciting new project which should be fully open this year. The site is located near Zambujeira do Mar, on the Alentejo coast. This is a highly ambitious initiative developed along very strict environmental lines. For example, renewable resources such as locally harvested timber and recycled plastic are used wherever possible and solar energy is used whenever practicable. Public indoor spaces have no air conditioning, but there is adequate cooling through underfloor ventilation and electric fans where possible. Pitches are 100 sq.m. and benefit from artificial shade. Caravans and wood-clad mobile homes are also available for rent. The swimming pool complex features a large outdoor pool and an indoor pool area with a wave machine and a wellness centre. The very large and innovative children's play park has climbing nets, labyrinths and caves. There is also a children's farm and a large play house. For adults, many sporting amenities will be available around the resort's 81-hectare park.

You might like to know

To explore Zmar's 81 hectares, bicycles are available for hire, with optional baby seats. There are bicycles suitable for all ages, as well as the necessary safety equipment.

☑ Walking notes or maps available
☐ Waymarked footpath – direct access from site
☐ Waymarked footpath within 1 km. of site
☐ Cycle trail – direct access from site
☑ Cycle trail access within 2 km. of site
☑ Mountain bike track within 2 km. of site
☑ Bicycle hire on site
☐ Accompanied hiking trips
☐ Accompanied cycling trips
☐ Drying room for wet clothes/boots
☐ Packed lunch service

Facilities: Eight toilet blocks provide comprehensive facilities, including those for children and disabled visitors. Bar. Restaurant. Crêperie. Takeaway. Large supermarket. Swimming pool. Covered pool. Wellness centre. Sports field. Games room. Play area, farm and play house. Tennis. Bicycle hire. Activity and entertainment programme. Mobile homes and caravans for rent. Caravan repair and servicing. The site's own debit card system is used for payment at all facilities. Off site: Vicentina coast and the Alentejo Natural Park. Sines (birthplace of Vasco de Gama). Cycle and walking tracks. Sea fishing.

Open: All year.

Directions: From the N120 from Odemira to Lagos, at roundabout in the centre of Portas de Transval turn towards Milfontes. Take turn to Cabo Sardão and then Zambujeira do Mar. Site is on the left. GPS: 37.60422, -8.73142

Charges guide

Per unit incl. up to 4 persons and electricity	€ 20,00 - € 50,00
extra person	€ 5,00 - € 10,00
child (4-12 yrs)	€ 5,00

Camping Markádia

Barragem de Odivelas, Apdo 17, P-7920-999 Alvito (Beja)
t: **284 763 141**   e: **markadia@hotmail.com**
alanrogers.com/PO8350   www.markadia.net

Accommodation: ☑ Pitch ☐ Mobile home/chalet   ☐ Hotel/B&B   ☐ Apartment

A tranquil, lakeside site in an unspoilt setting, this will appeal most to those nature lovers who want to 'get away from it all' and to those who enjoy country pursuits such as walking, fishing and riding. There are 130 casual unmarked pitches on undulating grass and sand with ample electricity connections (16A). The site is lit but a torch is required. The friendly Dutch owner has carefully planned the site so each pitch has its own oak tree to provide shade. The open countryside and lake provide excellent views and a very pleasant environment. The lake is in fact a 1,000-hectare reservoir, and more than 150 species of birds can be found in the area. The stellar views in the very low ambient lighting are wonderful at night. The bar/restaurant is open daily in season but weekends only during the winter. One can swim in the reservoir, and canoes, pedaloes and windsurfers are available for hire. You may bring your own boat, although power boats, quads and motor scooters are not allowed on environmental grounds.

You might like to know

There are plenty of quiet walking and cycle tracks locally – the site's owners will be pleased to recommend routes.

- ☑ **Walking notes or maps available**
- ☐ **Waymarked footpath – direct access from site**
- ☑ **Waymarked footpath within 1 km. of site**
- ☐ **Cycle trail – direct access from site**
- ☑ **Cycle trail access within 2 km. of site**
- ☐ **Mountain bike track within 2 km. of site**
- ☐ **Bicycle hire on site**
- ☐ **Accompanied hiking trips**
- ☐ **Accompanied cycling trips**
- ☐ **Drying room for wet clothes/boots**
- ☐ **Packed lunch service**

Facilities: Four modern, very clean and well equipped toilet blocks are built in traditional Portuguese style with hot water throughout. Washing machines. Motorcaravan services. Bar and restaurant (1/4-30/9). Shop (all year, bread to order). Lounge. Playground. Fishing. Boat hire. Tennis. Riding. Medical post. Car wash. Dogs are not accepted in July/Aug. Facilities and amenities may be reduced outside the main season.
Off site: Swimming and boating in the lake.

Open: All year.

Directions: From A2 between Setubal and the Algarve take exit 10 on IP8 (Ferreira and Beja). Take road to Torrao and 13 km. later, 1 km. north of Odivelas, turn right towards Barragem and site is 3 km. after crossing head of reservoir following small signs. GPS: 38.1812, -8.10293

Charges guide

Per unit incl. 2 persons and electricity	€ 25,70
extra person	€ 5,80
child (5-10 yrs)	€ 2,90
electricity	€ 2,90

No credit cards.

Parque de Campismo de Cerdeira

Rua de Cerdeira 400, P-4840 Campo do Gerês (Braga)
t: 253 351 005   e: info@parquecerdeira.com
alanrogers.com/PO8370   www.parquecerdeira.com

Accommodation: ☑Pitch   ☐ Mobile home/chalet   ☐ Hotel/B&B   ☐ Apartment

Located in the Peneda-Gerês National Park, amidst spectacular mountain scenery, this excellent site offers modern facilities in a truly natural area. The national park is home to all manner of flora, fauna and wildlife, including the roebuck, wolf and wild boar. The well fenced, professional and peaceful site offers good sized, unmarked, mostly level, grassy pitches in a shady woodland setting. Electricity is available for most pitches, though some long leads may be required. A very large timber complex, tastefully designed with the use of noble materials – granite and wood, provides a superb restaurant with a comprehensive menu. A pool with a separated section for toddlers is a welcome, cooling relief in the height of summer. There are unlimited opportunities in the immediate area for fishing, riding, canoeing, mountain biking and climbing, so take advantage of this quality mountain hospitality.

You might like to know

There are some wonderful quiet lanes in the vicinity of the site – perfect for cycling or walking.

☑ Walking notes or maps available
☐ Waymarked footpath – direct access from site
☑ Waymarked footpath within 1 km. of site
☐ Cycle trail – direct access from site
☑ Cycle trail access within 2 km. of site
☐ Mountain bike track within 2 km. of site
☐ Bicycle hire on site
☐ Accompanied hiking trips
☐ Accompanied cycling trips
☐ Drying room for wet clothes/boots
☐ Packed lunch service

Facilities: Three very clean sanitary blocks provide mixed style WCs, controllable showers and hot water. Good facilities for disabled visitors. Laundry. Gas supplies. Shop. Restaurant/bar. Outdoor pool (June-Sept). Playground. Bicycle hire. TV room (satellite). Medical post. Good tennis courts. Minigolf. Adventure park. Car wash. Barbecue areas. Torches useful. English spoken. Attractive bungalows to rent. WiFi in reception/bar area. Off site: Fishing and riding 800 m.

Open: All year.

Directions: From north, N103 (Braga-Chaves), turn left at N205 (7.5 km. north of Braga). Follow N205 to Caldelas Terras de Bouro and Covide where site is signed to Campo do Gerês. An eastern approach from N103 is for the adventurous but with magnificent views over mountains and lakes. GPS: 41.7631, -8.1905

Charges guide

Per unit incl. 2 persons and electricity	€ 13,05 - € 30,50
extra person	€ 3,20 - € 5,50
child (5-11 yrs)	€ 2,00 - € 3,30
dog	€ 1,50 - € 3,00

PORTUGAL – Ferreira do Zêzere

Camping Quinta da Cerejeira

Rua D. Maria Fernanda da Mota Cardoso 902, P-2240-333 Ferreira do Zêzere (Santarem)
t: 249 361 756   e: info@cerejeira.com
alanrogers.com/PO8550   www.cerejeira.com

Accommodation: ☑ Pitch ☐ Mobile home/chalet   ☐ Hotel/B&B ☑ Apartment

This is a delightful, small, family owned venture run by Gert and Teunie Verheij. It is
a converted farm (quinta) and has been coaxed into a very special campsite. The
pitches are on flat grass or on long terraces under fruit and olive trees. There are
25 pitches of which 18 have access to 6A electricity (long leads may be needed). There
is some shade and the site is full of rustic charm and craft works. It is very peaceful with
views of the surrounding green hills from the charming vine-covered patio above a small
swimming pool. You will notice the working well, no longer powered by a donkey but
you can see where he used to circle to pump water. The charming restaurant offers
a very reasonable menu of the day. This site has several rooms set aside for art and
craft activities, and quality workshops are offered in a range of subjects including
pottery, painting and Portuguese cooking. Visits are arranged to local vineyards and
we recommend a picnic at the nearby lake, which also offers all manner of watersports.
If you like a small peaceful, friendly site this is for you.

You might like to know
A number of trails start at Quinta da Cerejeira,
with others throughout Vila de Rei and in
the Parque Natural das Serras de Aire
e Candeeiros. Some routes are available for
downloading on your GPS-device.

☑ Walking notes or maps available
☑ Waymarked footpath – direct access from site
☐ Waymarked footpath within 1 km. of site
☐ Cycle trail – direct access from site
☑ Cycle trail access within 2 km. of site
☐ Mountain bike track within 2 km. of site
☐ Bicycle hire on site
☐ Accompanied hiking trips
☐ Accompanied cycling trips
☐ Drying room for wet clothes/boots
☐ Packed lunch service

Facilities: The single rustic sanitary building has
British style WCs with hot showers. It could be
busy at peak periods. Washing machine. No
facilities for disabled campers. No shop but just
ask and the baker calls daily. Self-service bar with
WiFi and library. Restaurant. Separate games and
rest room with satellite TV. Artistic workshops.
Swimming pool. Off site: Town with shops, bars
and restaurants and bus service 1 km. Fishing
and watersports 5 km. Riding 11 km.

Open: 1 February - 30 November.

Directions: From Lisbon take A1/A23 to Torres
Novas then IC3 to Tomar and N238 to Ferreira
do Zêzere. Take N348 to Vila de Rei and site is
1 km. from Ferreira do Zêzere to eastern side of
town (do not enter town). From Coimbra use
N238 road at an earlier exit.
GPS: 39.70075, -8.2782

Charges guide

Per unit incl. 2 persons and electricity	€ 16,25 - € 18,25
extra person	€ 3,50 - € 4,00
child (under 11 yrs)	€ 1,50 - € 2,00

ITALY – Lana

Camping Arquin

Feldgatterweg 25, I-39011 Lana (Trentino - Alto Adige)
t: 0473 561 187   e: info@camping-arquin.it
alanrogers.com/IT61865   www.camping-arquin.it

Accommodation: ☑Pitch ☐ Mobile home/chalet   ☐ Hotel/B&B   ☐ Apartment

Camping Arquin is in the South Tirol (Alto Adige) where the majority of the population speak German. It is open from early March to mid November and lies in an open valley surrounded by orchards, beyond which are high mountains. This is a region of natural beauty and is famous for its flowery meadows. The site is close to the village of Lana, one of the largest in the South Tirol and famous for its Mediterranean climate. There are 120 sunny, level, grass pitches up to 100 sq.m, all with 6A electricity and many are fully serviced. There is a wide range of marked footpaths and cycling routes. This is a good base for active families wishing to explore the local area on foot, by bicycle, in the car, by bus or by train (Bolzano 20 km.). The higher reaches of the mountains can be accessed by cable car. This area is also known for its thermal springs and baths. The interesting old town of Meran is only 7 km. away and is accessible by bus.

You might like to know
Why not take the cable car to the summit of Vigiljoch to enjoy wonderful panoramic views and an excellent descent on foot.

☑ Walking notes or maps available
☑ Waymarked footpath – direct access from site
☑ Waymarked footpath within 1 km. of site
☑ Cycle trail – direct access from site
☑ Cycle trail access within 2 km. of site
☑ Mountain bike track within 2 km. of site
☐ Bicycle hire on site
☐ Accompanied hiking trips
☐ Accompanied cycling trips
☐ Drying room for wet clothes/boots
☐ Packed lunch service

Facilities: Modern toilet block with all necessary facilities including those for babies and disabled visitors. Motorcaravan services. Small shop (15/3-5/11). Restaurant and bar (30/3-31/10). Small heated outdoor swimming pool (1/4-30/9). Play area. WiFi throughout (free). Charcoal barbecues not permitted. Off site: Bus stop 200 m. Large swimming pool 200 m. (May onwards; free to campers). Historical town of Meran 7 km. Museums. Golf and bicycle hire 2 km. Fishing 3 km. Hiking, Tennis. Paragliding. Rock climbing. Canoeing. Nature parks. Cable car.

Open: 1 March - 15 November.

Directions: Leave A22 Brenner motorway at Bozen Süd. Take expressway towards Meran. At the Lana-Burgstall exit turn left. After 250 m. take first right and follow signs to site. GPS: 46.611151, 11.174434

Charges guide

Per unit incl. 2 persons and electricity	€ 31,00 - € 35,00
dog	free

ITALY – Rasen

Camping Residence Corones

Niederrasen 124, I-39030 Rasen (Trentino - Alto Adige)
t: 047 449 6490 e: info@corones.com
alanrogers.com/IT61990 www.corones.com

Accommodation: ☑Pitch ☑Mobile home/chalet ☐ Hotel/B&B ☑ Apartment

Situated in a pine forest clearing at the foot of the attractive Antholz valley in the heart of German-speaking Südtirol, Corones is ideally situated both for winter sports enthusiasts and for walkers, cyclists, mountain bikers and those who prefer to explore the valleys and mountain roads of the Dolomites by car. There are 135 level pitches, all with 16A electricity and many also with water, drainage and satellite TV. The Residence offers luxury apartments and there are authentic Canadian log cabins for hire. The bar/restaurant and small shop are open all season. From the site you can see slopes which in winter become highly rated skiing pistes. A short drive up the broad Antholz/Anterselva valley takes you to an internationally important biathlon centre. An excellent day trip would be to drive up the valley and over the pass into Austria and then back via another pass. Back on site, a small pool and paddling pool could be very welcome. There is a regular programme of free excursions and occasional evening events are organised. Children's entertainment is provided in July and August.

You might like to know

Nature Fitness Park Kronplatz is Europe's largest Nordic Walking Park. There are 275 km. of well marked walking trails to be explored, with breathtaking views of the surrounding Dolomites.

- ☑ Walking notes or maps available
- ☐ Waymarked footpath – direct access from site
- ☑ Waymarked footpath within 1 km. of site
- ☐ Cycle trail – direct access from site
- ☑ Cycle trail access within 2 km. of site
- ☑ Mountain bike track within 2 km. of site
- ☐ Bicycle hire on site
- ☐ Accompanied hiking trips
- ☐ Accompanied cycling trips
- ☐ Drying room for wet clothes/boots
- ☐ Packed lunch service

Facilities: The central toilet block is traditional but well maintained and clean. Additional facilities below the Residence are of the highest quality including individual shower rooms with washbasins, washbasins with all WCs, a delightful children's unit and an excellent facility for disabled visitors. Fully equipped private shower rooms for hire. Luxurious wellness centre with saunas, solarium, jacuzzis, massage, therapy pools and heat benches. Heated outdoor swimming and paddling pools. Play area. WiFi throughout (charged). Charcoal barbecues are not permitted. Off site: Tennis 800 m. Bicycle hire 1 km. Riding and fishing 3 km.

Open: 6 December - 7 April,
8 May - 27 October.

Directions: Rasen/Rasun is 85 km. northeast of Bolzano. From Bressanone/Brixen exit on the A22 Brenner-Modena motorway, go east on SS49 for 50 km. then turn north (signed Rasen/Antholz). Turn immediately west at roundabout in Niederrasen/Rasun di Sotto to site on left in 100 m. GPS: 46.7758, 12.0367

Charges guide

Per unit incl. 2 persons, electricity on meter	€ 21,50 - € 32,50
extra person	€ 5,50 - € 8,20
child (3-15 yrs)	€ 3,00 - € 7,50

Camping Kiefernhain

Kiefernhain 37, I-39026 Prad am Stilfserjoch (Trentino - Alto Adige)
t: **047 361 6422** e: **kiefernhain@rolmail.net**
alanrogers.com/IT62060 www.camping-kiefernhain.it

Accommodation: ☑Pitch ☐ Mobile home/chalet ☐ Hotel/B&B ☐ Apartment

The Stelvio National Park is arguably Italy's premier Alpine park. Camping Kiefernhain lies within the park in the Val Venosta. There are 180 touring pitches here – some well shaded, others with much sunnier settings. Many pitches have fine views across to the Otztaler Alps. All have 6A electrical connections. A public swimming pool is adjacent to the site with free access for campers. Other amenities are available in a nearby sports centre or in the village, five minutes away on foot.

You might like to know

The Vinschgau region is ideal for mountain bikers, with miles of little known biking tracks along secluded forest paths and trails. One of the best downhill routes is Via Claudia Augusta from Lake Reschen to Meran, with a descent of over 1000 m.

☑ Walking notes or maps available
☐ Waymarked footpath – direct access from site
☑ Waymarked footpath within 1 km. of site
☐ Cycle trail – direct access from site
☑ Cycle trail access within 2 km. of site
☐ Mountain bike track within 2 km. of site
☐ Bicycle hire on site
☐ Accompanied hiking trips
☐ Accompanied cycling trips
☐ Drying room for wet clothes/boots
☐ Packed lunch service

Facilities: Bar/café and small shop. Playground. Guided walking excursions. Motorcaravan services. Off site: Swimming pool (free access). Bus stop 100 m. Village centre 300 m. Golf. Walking and cycling trails, mountain biking.

Open: Easter - 3 October.

Directions: From the A22 autostrada take the Bozen (south) exit and join the S38 passing Merano and Silandro. At Spondigna head south (still on the S38) to the village of Prato allo Stelvio, from where the site is well signed. GPS: 46.62536, 10.59485

Charges guide

Per unit incl. 2 persons and electricity	€ 25,60 - € 36,60
extra person	€ 6,50 - € 10,50
child (2-15 yrs)	€ 4,50 - € 6,50
dog	€ 3,50 - € 4,00

ITALY – Prad am Stilfserjoch

Camping Residence Sägemühle

Dornweg 12, I-39026 Prad am Stilfserjoch (Trentino - Alto Adige)
t: 047 361 6078   e: info@campingsaegemuehle.com
alanrogers.com/IT62070   www.campingsaegemuehle.com

Accommodation: ☑ Pitch ☐ Mobile home/chalet ☐ Hotel/B&B ☑ Apartment

This very attractive, well maintained site with beautiful mountain views is alongside a little village. The 160 grass touring pitches are neat and level, some have shade and most have electricity, water and drainage. The high standard indoor pool area is welcoming to cool oneself in the summer and relax in warm water after skiing in winter. The excellent facilities are cleverly placed under the pool area. New for the season is an enlarged reception, well equipped gym and a coffee bar with terrace leading to a very good restaurant. There is a new lift for those with mobility problems, although the facilities for disabled visitors are on ground level. Animation is provided in July and August and shared with a sister site. The area is renowned for its winter sports but has much to offer throughout the open season and reception will help with tourist information. The friendly owners speak some English and Dutch.

You might like to know

Cycle tours are available from South Tyrol Bike in the local village (from Monday to Friday) with qualified guides at a specially discounted price for campsite guests.

- ☑ Walking notes or maps available
- ☐ Waymarked footpath – direct access from site
- ☑ Waymarked footpath within 1 km. of site
- ☐ Cycle trail – direct access from site
- ☑ Cycle trail access within 2 km. of site
- ☑ Mountain bike track within 2 km. of site
- ☐ Bicycle hire on site
- ☐ Accompanied hiking trips
- ☐ Accompanied cycling trips
- ☐ Drying room for wet clothes/boots
- ☐ Packed lunch service

Facilities: The main and very modern sanitary facilities are under the pool complex. All WCs are British style and the showers are of high quality. Private cabins for hire. Facilities for disabled visitors. Children's facilities and baby baths. Washing machines. Restaurant and bar. Coffee bar with terrace. Indoor swimming pool with waves, jacuzzi and waterfall. Gym and sauna. Entertainment programme in season. Miniclub. Play areas. Internet. WiFi throughout (charged). Torches useful. Off site: Town facilities. Natural spring for paddling 800 m. Bicycle hire 300 m. Riding 800 m. Golf 30 km.

Open: All year excl. 8 November - 19 December.

Directions: Site is west of Bolzano. From A38/S40 west of Bolzano, take exit for Pso dello Stelvio/Stilfserjoch (also marked S38) and village of Prad am Stilfserjoch. Site is well signed from here. GPS: 46.617628, 10.595317

Charges guide

Per unit incl. 2 persons and electricity	€ 27,60 - € 41,10
extra person	€ 8,00 - € 11,00
child (2-15 yrs)	€ 5,50 - € 9,00
dog	€ 3,50 - € 5,00

ITALY – Laives/Leifers

Camping-Park Steiner

J. F. Kennedy Strasse 32, I-39055 Laives/Leifers (Trentino - Alto Adige)
t: 047 195 0105 e: info@campingsteiner.com
alanrogers.com/IT62100 www.campingsteiner.com

Accommodation: ☑Pitch ☑Mobile home/chalet ☑Hotel/B&B ☐ Apartment

The welcoming Camping Steiner is very central for touring with the whole of the Dolomite region within easy reach. With much on-site activity, one could spend an enjoyable holiday here, especially now the SS12, by which it stands, has a motorway alternative. The 180 individual touring pitches, mostly with good shade and hardstanding, are in rows with easy access and all have 6A electricity. There are also 30 chalets available to rent. There is a family style pizzeria/restaurant, and indoor and outdoor pools. The Steiner Park Hotel provides another restaurant, café and full hotel facilities. This friendly, family run site has a long tradition of providing a happy camping experience in the more traditional style – the owner remembers Alan Rogers who stayed here on many occasions. We met a Danish couple during our visit who were staying for five weeks as it is so easy to get to different parts of the Dolomites and is ideal for walking.

You might like to know

Cycle from Austria (Passo Resia or Passo del Brennero) to Lake Garda! You can also return by train to Camping Steiner.

☑ Walking notes or maps available
☑ Waymarked footpath – direct access from site
☑ Waymarked footpath within 1 km. of site
☐ Cycle trail – direct access from site
☑ Cycle trail access within 2 km. of site
☑ Mountain bike track within 2 km. of site
☑ Bicycle hire on site
☑ Accompanied hiking trips
☑ Accompanied cycling trips
☑ Drying room for wet clothes/boots
☑ Packed lunch service

Facilities: The two sanitary blocks are equipped to a high standard, one having been completely refurbished. They can be heated in cool weather. Shop, bar/pizzeria/restaurant with takeaway (23/3-30/10). Outdoor pool, with paddling pool, and a smaller covered heated pool (all season). Playground. Bicycle hire. Dogs are not accepted in July/Aug. Off site: Fishing 2.5 km. Riding 12 km. Golf and skiing 28 km.

Open: 16 March - 31 October.

Directions: Site is by the SS12 on northern edge of Leifers, 8 km. south of Bolzano. If approaching from north, at the Bolzano-Süd exit from A22 Brenner-Modena motorway follow Trento signs for 7 km. From south on motorway take Ora exit, then north on SS12 towards Bolzano for 14 km. GPS: 46.42955, 11.34380

Charges guide

Per unit incl. 2 persons and electricity	€ 28,00 - € 35,00
extra person	€ 7,00 - € 9,00
child (under 9 yrs)	free - € 6,00

ITALY – Calceranica al Lago

Camping Punta Lago

Via Lungo Lago 42, I-38050 Calceranica al Lago (Trentino - Alto Adige)
t: 046 172 3229 e: info@campingpuntalago.com
alanrogers.com/IT62260 www.campingpuntalago.com

Accommodation: ☑ Pitch ☑ Mobile home/chalet ☐ Hotel/B&B ☐ Apartment

Camping Punta Lago is in a beautiful setting on Lago di Caldonazzo. This attractive family run campsite, with easy lake access across a small road, has 140 level, shaded pitches on grass. Of a good size, all have 3/6A electricity and 50 are serviced with water and drainage. The campsite first opened 45 years ago and brothers Gino and Mauro continue the friendly family tradition of ensuring you enjoy your holiday. As President of the Consortia Trentino Outdoors, Gino knows all about the range of activities available locally including fishing, lake swimming, windsurfing, sailing and canoeing. There are excellent restaurants within 50 m. of the gate. The site itself has a large terraced snack bar with wonderful views of the lake and the most amazing ice cream (gelato), yoghurt and fruit concoctions.

You might like to know

Mountain bike hire is available on site, with a free workshop facility.

- ☑ Walking notes or maps available
- ☐ Waymarked footpath – direct access from site
- ☑ Waymarked footpath within 1 km. of site
- ☐ Cycle trail – direct access from site
- ☑ Cycle trail access within 2 km. of site
- ☐ Mountain bike track within 2 km. of site
- ☑ Bicycle hire on site
- ☐ Accompanied hiking trips
- ☐ Accompanied cycling trips
- ☐ Drying room for wet clothes/boots
- ☐ Packed lunch service

Facilities: One central sanitary block has superb facilities with hot water throughout. Well designed bathroom and washbasin area. Excellent facilities for disabled visitors and babies. Private units for rent, some with massage baths. Laundry facilities. Freezer. Shop. Bar/snack bar. Fishing (with permit). Comprehensive play area. Animation programme (July/Aug). Internet access. WiFi throughout (charged). Cinema. TV. Off site: Bicycle hire, town and ATM 1 km. Watersports. Riding 3 km. Golf 20 km. Train 1 km. to Venice and other cities.

Open: 1 May - 15 September.

Directions: From A22 Bolzano-Trento autostrada take SS47 towards Padova. After 15 km. turn for Lago di Caldonazzo and Calceranica al Lago. Approaching from west by the railway, continue along Via Donegani, turn left at Esso station into Via al Lago and right at lakeside into Via Lungo Lago. Site is on right. From the east follow Calceranica then turn right just before Esso station. GPS: 46.00230, 11.25450

Charges guide

Per unit incl. 2 persons and electricity	€ 16,00 - € 40,00
extra person	€ 5,00 - € 9,00
child (2-12 yrs)	€ 4,00 - € 7,00

ITALY – Levico Terme

Camping Lago di Levico

Localitá Pleina, I-38056 Levico Terme (Trentino - Alto Adige)
t: 046 170 6491 e: info@campinglevico.com
alanrogers.com/IT62290 www.campinglevico.com

Accommodation: ☑Pitch ☑Mobile home/chalet ☐ Hotel/B&B ☐ Apartment

Camping Lago di Levico, by a pretty lakeside in the mountains, is the merger of two popular sites, Camping Levico and Camping Jolly. Brothers Andrea and Geno Antoniolli are making great improvements, already there is an impressive new reception and further developments of the lakeside and swimming areas are planned. The lakeside pitches are quite special. There are 430 mostly grassy and shaded pitches (70-120 sq.m) with 6A electricity, 150 also have water and drainage and 12 have private facilities. Staff are welcoming and fluent in English. The swimming pool complex is popular, as is the summer family entertainment. There is a small supermarket on site and it is a short distance to the local village. The restaurant, bar, pizzeria and takeaway are open all season. The beautiful grass shores of the lake are ideal for sunbathing and the crystal clear water is ideal for enjoying (non-motorised) water activities. This is a site where the natural beauty of an Italian lake can be enjoyed without being overwhelmed by commercial tourism.

You might like to know

Various bikes are available for rent on site, including high quality mountain bikes. There is also a good repair and maintenance facility.

- ☑ Walking notes or maps available
- ☐ Waymarked footpath – direct access from site
- ☐ Waymarked footpath within 1 km. of site
- ☑ Cycle trail – direct access from site
- ☑ Cycle trail access within 2 km. of site
- ☑ Mountain bike track within 2 km. of site
- ☑ Bicycle hire on site
- ☑ Accompanied hiking trips
- ☐ Accompanied cycling trips
- ☐ Drying room for wet clothes/boots
- ☐ Packed lunch service

Facilities: Four modern sanitary blocks provide hot water for showers, washbasins and washing. Mostly British style toilets. Single locked unit for disabled visitors. Laundry facilities. Freezer. Motorcaravan service point. Good shop. Bar/restaurant and takeaway. Outdoor swimming pool. Play area. Miniclub and entertainment (high season). Fishing. Satellite TV and cartoon cinema. Internet access (free in low season). Kayak hire. Tennis. Torches useful. Bicycle hire. Off site: Boat launching 500 m. Bicycle track 1.5 km. Town with all the usual facilities and ATM 2 km. Riding 3 km. Golf 7 km.

Open: 15 April - 10 October.

Directions: From A22 Verona-Bolzano road take turn for Trento on S47 to Levico Terme where campsite is very well signed.
GPS: 46.00799, 11.28454

Charges guide

Per unit incl. 2 persons and electricity	€ 9,50 - € 38,00
extra person	€ 3,00 - € 14,25
child (3-11 yrs)	free - € 6,50
dog	free - € 5,00

Camping Dei Fiori

Viale Riviera 11, I-17027 Pietra Ligure (Ligúria)
t: **019 625 636** e: **info@campingdeifiori.it**
alanrogers.com/IT64040   www.campingdeifiori.it

Accommodation: ☑Pitch ☑Mobile home/chalet ☐ Hotel/B&B ☐ Apartment

This is a small, family owned site with basic facilities, situated around 500 metres from the beach in an old olive yard and offering reasonable prices for your stay. A road runs past the entrance and the restaurant terrace is partly overlooked by an elevated section of this road. There are 232 pitches, which are on the small side, with lots of seasonal pitches for Italian campers, and some bungalows. The 60 flat touring pitches are mainly on the lower terraces of the site, with some shade and 6A electricity. Some of the smallest pitches may be challenging when manoeuvring with large units. The restaurant overlooks the pool on one side of the main site road close to the entrance. On the opposite side of the road is a small bar serving drinks and snacks. Daniele and Deborah, the friendly owners, will assist in any way they can to ensure you enjoy your stay here. The swimming pool and a paddling pool provide an alternative to the beach, where a free shuttle service brings you back in the afternoon.

You might like to know

The inland landscape here is breathtaking and a number of guided walks and cycle trips are organised. There is a good repair and bike washing area on site.

☑ Walking notes or maps available
☐ Waymarked footpath – direct access from site
☑ Waymarked footpath within 1 km. of site
☐ Cycle trail – direct access from site
☑ Cycle trail access within 2 km. of site
☐ Mountain bike track within 2 km. of site
☑ Bicycle hire on site
☐ Accompanied hiking trips
☑ Accompanied cycling trips
☐ Drying room for wet clothes/boots
☐ Packed lunch service

Facilities: Two blocks are old and provide a mixture of British and Turkish toilets. However a new Portacabin-style unit offers better showers and toilets although the majority are Turkish. Water is solar heated and free throughout. The facilities can be under pressure at peak times. Sinks have cold water only. Facilities are provided, but we do not recommend this site for disabled campers. Motorcaravan service point. Fridges for use by campers. Bar/snack bar. Takeaway (June-Sept). Shop. Swimming pool (May-Sept) and fabric paddling pool. Limited entertainment programme in season. Bicycle hire. Off site: Beach and town 550 m. Riding 8 km. Golf 10 km.

Open: All year.

Directions: From the A10/E80 take Pietra Ligure exit between Finale Ligure and Loano. Site is just southwest of the town of Pietra Ligure and is clearly signed off the beach road onto a minor road heading northwest.
GPS: 44.14183, 8.27833

Charges guide

Per unit incl. 3 persons and electricity	€ 23,00 - € 41,00
extra person	€ 5,00 - € 8,00
child (4-10 yrs)	€ 4,00 - € 7,00

No credit cards.

Camping Bled

Kidriceva 10c SI, SLO-4260 Bled
t: 045 752 000   e: info@camping-bled.com
alanrogers.com/SV4200   www.camping-bled.com

Accommodation: ☑Pitch ☑Mobile home/chalet   ☐ Hotel/B&B   ☐ Apartment

On the western tip of Lake Bled is Camping Bled. The waterfront here has a small public beach, immediately behind which runs a gently sloping narrow wooded valley. Pitches at the front, used mainly for overnighters, are now marked, separated by trees and enlarged, bringing the total number to 280. In areas at the back, visitors are free to pitch where they like. There is some noise from trains as they trundle out of a high tunnel overlooking the campsite on the line from Bled to Bohinj. But this is a small price to pay for the pleasure of being in a pleasant site from which the lake, its famous little island, its castle and town can be explored on foot or by boat. Unlike many other Slovenian sites, the number of statics (and semi-statics) here appears to be carefully controlled with touring caravans, motorcaravans and tents predominating.

You might like to know

A trained mountain bike guide is on hand to assist with cycling tours, as well as the transfer of bicycles and baggage if necessary.

- ☑ Walking notes or maps available
- ☐ Waymarked footpath – direct access from site
- ☑ Waymarked footpath within 1 km. of site
- ☐ Cycle trail – direct access from site
- ☑ Cycle trail access within 2 km. of site
- ☐ Mountain bike track within 2 km. of site
- ☐ Bicycle hire on site
- ☑ Accompanied hiking trips
- ☑ Accompanied cycling trips
- ☑ Drying room for wet clothes/boots
- ☐ Packed lunch service

Facilities: Toilet facilities in five blocks are of a high standard (with free hot showers). Three blocks are heated. Private bathrooms for rent. Solar energy used. Washing machines and dryers. Motorcaravan services. Gas supplies. Fridge hire. Supermarket. Restaurant. Play area and children's zoo. Games hall. Trampolines. Organised activities in July/Aug including children's club, excursions and sporting activities. Mountain bike tours. Live entertainment. Fishing. Bicycle hire. Free WiFi over site. Off site: Riding 3 km. Golf 5 km. Within walking distance of waterfront and town. Restaurants nearby.

Open: 1 April - 15 October.

Directions: From the town of Bled drive along south shore of lake to its western extremity (some 2 km) to the site.
GPS: 46.36155, 14.08075

Charges guide

Per unit incl. 2 persons and electricity	€ 21,50 - € 31,80
extra person	€ 8,90 - € 12,90
child (7-13 yrs)	€ 6,23 - € 9,03
dog	€ 3,00

SLOVENIA – Soca

Kamp Klin

Lepena 1, SLO-5232 Soca
t: 053 889 513 e: kampklin@siol.net
alanrogers.com/SV4235

Accommodation: ☑Pitch ☑Mobile home/chalet ☐ Hotel/B&B ☐ Apartment

With an attractive location surrounded by mountains in the Triglav National Park, Kamp Klin is next to the confluence of the Soca and Lepenca rivers, which makes it an ideal base for fishing, kayaking and rafting. The campsite has 50 pitches, all for tourers, with 7A electricity, on one large, grassy field, connected by a circular, gravel access road. It is attractively landscaped with flowers and young trees, which provide some shade. Some pitches are right on the bank of the river (unfenced) and there are beautiful views of the river and the mountains. Kamp Klin is privately owned and there is a 'pension' next door, all run by the Zorc family, who serve the local dishes with compe (potatoes), cottage cheese, grilled trout and local salami in the restaurant. From the site it is only a short drive to the highest point of Slovenia, the Triglav mountain and its beautiful viewpoint with marked walking routes. Like so many Slovenian sites in this area, this is a good holiday base for the active camper.

You might like to know

There are some great walks in the surrounding mountains – something to suit all abilities.

☑ Walking notes or maps available
☑ Waymarked footpath – direct access from site
☐ Waymarked footpath within 1 km. of site
☐ Cycle trail – direct access from site
☑ Cycle trail access within 2 km. of site
☐ Mountain bike track within 2 km. of site
☐ Bicycle hire on site
☐ Accompanied hiking trips
☐ Accompanied cycling trips
☐ Drying room for wet clothes/boots
☐ Packed lunch service

Facilities: One modern toilet block and a Portacabin style unit with toilets and controllable showers. Laundry with sinks. Bar/restaurant. Play field. Fishing (permit required). Torch useful. Off site: Riding 500 m. Bicycle hire 10 km.

Open: March - October.

Directions: Site is on the main Kranjska Gora-Bovec road and is well signed 3 km. east of Soca. Access is via a sharp turn from the main road and over a small bridge. GPS: 46.33007, 13.644

Charges guide

Per person	€ 11,00 - € 13,00
child (7-12 yrs)	€ 5,50 - € 6,50
electricity	€ 3,50

SLOVENIA – Kobarid

Kamp Koren Kobarid

Ladra 1b, SLO-5222 Kobarid
t: 053 891 311   e: info@kamp-koren.si
alanrogers.com/SV4270   www.kamp-koren.si

Accommodation: ☑Pitch ☑Mobile home/chalet ☐ Hotel/B&B ☐ Apartment

Superbly run by its owner, Lidija Koren, this peaceful, well shaded site is located above the Soca river gorge in the countryside close to Kobarid. A small site with 90 pitches, it is deservedly very popular with those interested in outdoor sports, including hiking, mountain biking, paragliding, canoeing, canyoning, rafting and fishing. At the same time, its quiet location makes it a good site for those seeking a relaxing break. Six attractive, well equipped chalets are a recent addition. The Julian Alps, and in particular the Triglav National Park, is a wonderful and under-explored part of Slovenia that has much to offer. Kobarid, probably best approached via Udine in Italy, is a pleasant country town, with easy access to nearby rivers, valleys and mountains, which alone justify a visit to Kamp Koren. But most British visitors will remember it for the opportunity it provides to fill that curious gap in their knowledge of European history. The local museum in Kobarid was recently voted European Museum of the Year and is excellent.

You might like to know

Top quality mountain bikes are available for rent. 2012 rates were €15 per day and €10 per half day.

- ☑ Walking notes or maps available
- ☐ Waymarked footpath – direct access from site
- ☑ Waymarked footpath within 1 km. of site
- ☐ Cycle trail – direct access from site
- ☑ Cycle trail access within 2 km. of site
- ☑ Mountain bike track within 2 km. of site
- ☑ Bicycle hire on site
- ☐ Accompanied hiking trips
- ☐ Accompanied cycling trips
- ☐ Drying room for wet clothes/boots
- ☐ Packed lunch service

Facilities: Two attractive and well maintained log-built toilet blocks. Facilities for disabled visitors. Laundry facilities. Motorcaravan services. Shop (March-Nov). Café dispenses light meals, snacks and drinks apparently with flexible closing hours. Play area. Bowling. Fishing. Bicycle hire. Canoe hire. Climbing walls. Communal barbecue. WiFi. Off site: Town within walking distance. Riding 5 km. Golf 20 km. Guided tours in the Soca valley and around Slovenia start from the site.

Open: All year.

Directions: Approaching Kobarid from Tolmin on 102, just before Kobarid turn right on 203 towards Bovec and after 100 m. take descending slip road to right and keep more or less straight on to Napoléon's bridge (about 500 m). Cross bridge and site is on left, 100 m. GPS: 46.25075, 13.58658

Charges guide

Per unit incl. 2 persons and electricity	€ 24,00 - € 27,00
dog	€ 2,00

Camping Menina

Varpolje 105, SLO-3332 Recica ob Savinji
t: 035 835 027 e: info@campingmenina.com
alanrogers.com/SV4405 www.campingmenina.com

Accommodation: ☑Pitch ☑Mobile home/chalet ☑Hotel/B&B ☐ Apartment

Camping Menina is in the heart of the 35 km. long Upper Savinja Valley, surrounded by 2,500 m. high mountains and unspoilt nature. It is being improved every year by the young, enthusiastic owner, Jurij Kolenc and has 200 pitches, all for touring units, on grassy fields under mature trees and with access from gravel roads. All have 6-10A electricity. The Savinja river runs along one side of the site, but if its water is too cold for swimming, the site also has a lake which can be used for swimming. This site is a perfect base for walking or mountain biking in the mountains. A wealth of maps and routes are available from reception. Rafting, canyoning and kayaking, and visits to a fitness studio, sauna and massage salon are organised. The site is now open all year to offer skiing holidays.

You might like to know

Roads between the valleys around the site offer around 1,000 km. combinations of cycle friendly routes. The site has a partnership with a cycling holiday organiser and various excursions are possible, including downhill-only trips – or, for the very keen, uphill-only trips!

- ☑ Walking notes or maps available
- ☐ Waymarked footpath – direct access from site
- ☑ Waymarked footpath within 1 km. of site
- ☐ Cycle trail – direct access from site
- ☑ Cycle trail access within 2 km. of site
- ☑ Mountain bike track within 2 km. of site
- ☑ Bicycle hire on site
- ☐ Accompanied hiking trips
- ☑ Accompanied cycling trips
- ☐ Drying room for wet clothes/boots
- ☐ Packed lunch service

Facilities: Two toilet blocks (one new) have modern fittings with toilets, open plan washbasins and controllable hot showers. Motorcaravan service point. Bar/restaurant with open-air terrace (evenings only) and open-air kitchen. Sauna. Playing field. Play area. Fishing. Mountain bike hire. Russian bowling. Excursions (52). Live music and gatherings around the camp fire. Indian village. Hostel. Skiing in winter. Kayaking. Mobile homes to rent. Climbing wall. Rafting. Off site: Fishing 2 km. Recica and other villages with much culture and folklore are close. Indian sauna at Coze.

Open: All year.

Directions: From Ljubljana/Celje autobahn A1. Exit at Sentupert and turn north towards Mozirje (14 km). At roundabout just before Mozirje, hard left staying on the 225 for 6 km. to Nizka then just after the circular automatic petrol station, left where site is signed. GPS: 46.31168, 14.90913

Charges guide

Per unit incl. 2 persons	
and electricity	€ 17,80 - € 23,00
extra person	€ 7,50 - € 10,00
child (5-15 yrs)	€ 3,50 - € 6,00
dog	€ 2,50 - € 3,00

Balatontourist Camping Füred

Széchenyi út 24., H-8230 Balatonfüred (Veszprem County)
t: 87 580 241   e: fured@balatontourist.hu
alanrogers.com/HU5090   www.balatontourist.hu

Accommodation: ☑Pitch ☑Mobile home/chalet ☑Hotel/B&B ☑Apartment

This is a large international holiday village rather than just a campsite. Pleasantly decorated with flowers and shrubs, it offers a very wide range of facilities and sporting activities. All that one could want for a family holiday can be found here. The 890 individual pitches (60-120 sq.m), all with electricity (6/10A), are on either side of hard access roads on which pitch numbers are painted. Many bungalows are for rent. Mature trees cover about two thirds of the site giving shade, with the remaining area being in the open. Directly on the lake with 800 m. of access for boats and bathing, there is a large, grassy area for relaxation, a small beach area for children and a variety of watersports. A water-ski drag lift is most spectacular with its four towers erected in the lake to pull skiers around the circuit. There is a swimming pool on site with lifeguards. Along the main road that runs through the site are shops and kiosks, with the main bar/restaurant and terrace overlooking the lake. Other bars and restaurants are around the site. Coach trips and pleasure cruises are organised.

You might like to know
Lake Balaton is Central Europe's largest lake and there are miles of excellent cycle tracks around much of its perimeter.

- ☑ Walking notes or maps available
- ☐ Waymarked footpath – direct access from site
- ☑ Waymarked footpath within 1 km. of site
- ☐ Cycle trail – direct access from site
- ☑ Cycle trail access within 2 km. of site
- ☐ Mountain bike track within 2 km. of site
- ☐ Bicycle hire on site
- ☐ Accompanied hiking trips
- ☐ Accompanied cycling trips
- ☐ Drying room for wet clothes/boots
- ☐ Packed lunch service

Facilities: Five fully equipped toilet blocks around the site include hot water for dishwashing and laundry (cleaning and maintenance variable). Private cabins for rent. Laundry service. Numerous bars, restaurants, cafés, food bars and supermarket (15/5-15/9). Stalls and kiosks with wide range of goods and souvenirs. Excellent swimming pool (1/6-31/8). Sandy beach. Large free water chute. Animation for children. Sports activities organised for adults. Sauna. Fishing. Water ski lift. Windsurf school. Sailing. Pedalos. Play area. Bicycle hire. Tennis. Minigolf. Video games. WiFi throughout (charged). Dogs are not accepted. Off site: Close by a street of fast food bars, about ten in all, offering a variety of Hungarian and international dishes. Riding and golf 10 km.

Open: 27 April - 30 September.

Directions: Site is just south of Balatonfüred, at the traffic circle on Balatonfüred-Tihany road is well signed. Gates closed 13.00-15.00 except at weekends. GPS: 46.94565, 17.87709

Charges guide

Per unit incl. 2 persons and electricity	HUF 3600 - 9200
extra person	HUF 800 - 1600
child (2-14 yrs)	HUF 500 - 1200

HUNGARY – Révfülöp

Balatontourist Camping Napfény

Halász ut. 5, H-8253 Révfülöp (Veszprem County)
t: 87 563 031   e: napfeny@balatontourist.hu
alanrogers.com/HU5370   www.balatontourist.hu

Accommodation: ☑ Pitch ☑ Mobile home/chalet ☐ Hotel/B&B ☐ Apartment

Camping Napfény, an exceptionally good site, is designed for families with children of all ages looking for an active holiday, and has a 200 m. frontage on Lake Balaton. The site's 370 pitches vary in size (60-110 sq.m) and almost all have shade – very welcome during the hot Hungarian summers – and 6-10A electricity. As with most of the sites on Lake Balaton, a train line runs just outside the site boundary. There are steps to get into the lake and canoes, boats and pedaloes for hire. An extensive entertainment programme is designed for all ages and there are several bars and restaurants of various styles. There are souvenir shops and a supermarket. In fact, you need not leave the site at all during your holiday, although there are several excursions on offer, including to Budapest or to one of the many Hungarian spas, a trip over Lake Balaton or a traditional wine tour.

You might like to know
This excellent site has a wide range of activities on offer, including canoeing and rowing, as well as bicycle hire.

☑ Walking notes or maps available
☐ Waymarked footpath – direct access from site
☑ Waymarked footpath within 1 km. of site
☐ Cycle trail – direct access from site
☑ Cycle trail access within 2 km. of site
☐ Mountain bike track within 2 km. of site
☑ Bicycle hire on site
☐ Accompanied hiking trips
☐ Accompanied cycling trips
☐ Drying room for wet clothes/boots
☐ Packed lunch service

Facilities: The three excellent sanitary blocks have toilets, washbasins (open style and in cabins) with hot and cold water, spacious showers (both preset and controllable), child sized toilets and basins, and two bathrooms (hourly charge). Heated baby room. Facilities for disabled campers. Launderette. Dog shower. Motorcaravan services. Supermarket, souvenir shop and several bars (all 1/6-31/8). Restaurants. Children's pool. Sports field. Minigolf. Fishing. Bicycle hire. Canoe, rowing boat and pedalo hire. Extensive entertainment programme for all ages. WiFi throughout (charged). Off site: Tennis 300 m. Riding 3 km. Golf 20 km.

Open: 27 April - 30 September.

Directions: Follow road 71 from Veszprém southeast to Keszthely. Site is in Révfülöp. GPS: 46.829469, 17.640164

Charges guide

Per unit incl. 2 persons and electricity	HUF 3600 - 7150
extra person	HUF 850 - 1200
child (2-14 yrs)	HUF 550 - 950
dog	HUF 550 - 950

Camping le Bivouac

Route des Paccots 21, CH-1618 Châtel-Saint Denis (Fribourg)
t: 021 948 7849   e: info@le-bivouac.ch
alanrogers.com/CH9300   www.le-bivouac.ch

Accommodation: ☑Pitch ☐ Mobile home/chalet ☐ Hotel/B&B ☐ Apartment

A pleasant little site in the forested mountains above Montreux and Vevey on Lac Leman (Lake Geneva). Le Bivouac has its own small swimming pool and children's pool. Most of the places here are taken by seasonal caravans (130) interspersed with about 30 pitches for tourists. Electrical connections (10A) are available and there are five water points. Due to access difficulties, the site is not open to tourers in winter. The active can take mountain walks in the area, or set off to explore Montreux and the lake. Others will enjoy the peace and quiet of this green hideaway. M. Fivaz, the owner, speaks excellent English and is only too happy to suggest local activities.

You might like to know

This area offers a good selection of walks, generally of a fairly undemanding nature. Walking is the best way to appreciate the area fully, and it need not be too strenuous if combined with one of the mountain trains or cable cars.

☑ Walking notes or maps available
☑ Waymarked footpath – direct access from site
☐ Waymarked footpath within 1 km. of site
☐ Cycle trail – direct access from site
☑ Cycle trail access within 2 km. of site
☐ Mountain bike track within 2 km. of site
☐ Bicycle hire on site
☐ Accompanied hiking trips
☐ Accompanied cycling trips
☑ Drying room for wet clothes/boots
☐ Packed lunch service

Facilities: The good toilet facilities in the main building include free preset hot water in washbasins, showers and sinks for laundry and dishes. Washing machine and dryer. Gas supplies. Shop (1/7-31/8, bread to order). Bar (1/6-30/9). Swimming pool and paddling pool (15/6-15/9). TV. Table football. Fishing in adjacent stream (licence from reception). Internet and WiFi. Off site: Bus to Chatel stops at the gate. Bicycle hire 3 km. Riding 10 km.

Open: 1 May - 30 September.

Directions: From motorway 12/E27 (Bern-Vevey) take Châtel St Denis exit no. 2 and turn towards Les Paccots (1 km). Site is on left up hill. GPS: 46.52513, 6.91828

Charges guide

Per person	CHF 6,50
child (6-16 yrs)	CHF 4,50
pitch	CHF 16,50
electricity	CHF 4,50

No credit cards. Euros are accepted.

Camping Grassi

Grassiweg 60, CH-3714 Frutigen (Bern)
t: 033 671 1149 e: campinggrassi@bluewin.ch
alanrogers.com/CH9360 www.camping-grassi.ch

Accommodation: ☑Pitch ☐ Mobile home/chalet ☐ Hotel/B&B ☐ Apartment

This is a small site with about half the pitches occupied by static caravans, used by their owners for weekends and holidays. The 70 or so places available for tourists are not marked out but it is said that the site is not allowed to become overcrowded. Most places are on level grass with two small terraces at the end of the site. There is little shade but the site is set in a river valley with trees on the hills which enclose the area. Electricity is available for all pitches but long leads may be required in parts. It would make a useful overnight stop en-route for Kandersteg and the railway station where cars can join the train for transportation through the Lotschberg Tunnel to the Rhône Valley and Simplon Pass, or for a longer stay to explore the Bernese Oberland.

You might like to know
This is a good starting point for mountain walks along the north or south wall of the Lötschbergbahn.

☑ Walking notes or maps available
☑ Waymarked footpath – direct access from site
☐ Waymarked footpath within 1 km. of site
☑ Cycle trail – direct access from site
☐ Cycle trail access within 2 km. of site
☑ Mountain bike track within 2 km. of site
☑ Bicycle hire on site
☐ Accompanied hiking trips
☐ Accompanied cycling trips
☑ Drying room for wet clothes/boots
☐ Packed lunch service

Facilities: The well constructed, heated sanitary block is of good quality. Washing machine and dryer. Gas supplies. Motorcaravan services. Communal room with TV. Kiosk (1/7-31/8). Play area and play house. Mountain bike hire. Fishing. Bicycle hire. WiFi. Off site: Shops and restaurants 10 minutes walk away in village. Riding 2 km. Outdoor and indoor pools, tennis and minigolf in Frutigen. A new sauna and wellness centre has recently opened in the village. Skiing and walking.

Open: All year.

Directions: Take Kandersteg road from Spiez and leave at Frutigen Dorf exit from where site is signed. GPS: 46.58173, 7.64219

Charges guide

Per unit incl. 2 persons and electricity	CHF 25,80 - 32,30
extra person	CHF 6,40
child (1-16 yrs)	CHF 1,50 - 3,20
dog	CHF 1,50

Camping Manor Farm 1

Seestrassee 201, CH-3800 Interlaken-Thunersee (Bern)
t: 033 822 2264 e: manorfarm1@swisscamps.ch
alanrogers.com/CH9420 www.manorfarm.ch

Accommodation: ☑Pitch ☑Mobile home/chalet ☐ Hotel/B&B ☑ Apartment

Manor Farm has been popular with British visitors for many years, as this is one of the traditional touring areas of Switzerland. The flat terrain is divided into 525 individual, numbered pitches, which vary considerably, both in size (60-100 sq.m) and price. There is shade in some places. There are 144 pitches with electricity (4/13A), water and drainage, and 55 also have cable TV connections. Reservations can be made, although you should find space, except perhaps in late July/early August when the best places may be taken. Around 40 per cent of the pitches are taken by permanent or letting units and a tour operator. The site lies outside the town on the northern side of the Thuner See, with most of the site between the road and lake but with one part on the far side of the road. Interlaken is very much a tourist town, but the area is rich in scenery with innumerable mountain excursions and walks available. The lakes and Jungfrau railway are near at hand. Manor Farm is a large campsite, efficiently run with a minimum of formality and would suit those looking for an active family holiday.

You might like to know

There are many excellent mountain railways in the area and good local bus connections throughout the year.

- ☑ Walking notes or maps available
- ☑ Waymarked footpath – direct access from site
- ☐ Waymarked footpath within 1 km. of site
- ☑ Cycle trail – direct access from site
- ☐ Cycle trail access within 2 km. of site
- ☐ Mountain bike track within 2 km. of site
- ☑ Bicycle hire on site
- ☐ Accompanied hiking trips
- ☐ Accompanied cycling trips
- ☑ Drying room for wet clothes/boots
- ☐ Packed lunch service

Facilities: Seven separate toilet blocks are heated and fully equipped. They include free hot water for baths and showers. Twenty private toilet units are for rent. Laundry facilities. Motorcaravan services. Gas supplies. Shop (1/4-15/10). Site-owned restaurant adjacent (1/3-30/10). Snack bar with takeaway (1/7-20/8). TV room. Playground and paddling pool. Minigolf. Bicycle hire. Sailing and windsurfing school. Lake swimming. Boat hire (slipway for campers' own). Fishing. Daily activities and entertainment in high season. Max. 1 dog. WiFi (charged). Off site: Golf (18 holes) 500 m. (handicap card). Riding 3 km. Good area for cycling and walking.

Open: All year.

Directions: Site is 3 km. west of Interlaken along the road running north of the Thuner See towards Thun. Follow signs for 'Camp 1'. From A8 (bypassing Interlaken) take exit 24 marked 'Gunten, Beatenberg', which is a spur road bringing you out close to site.
GPS: 46.68129, 7.81524

Charges guide

Per unit incl. 2 persons and electricity	CHF 37,00 - 63,50
extra person	CHF 10,50
child (6-15 yrs)	CHF 5,00

Camping Lazy Rancho 4

Lehnweg 6, CH-3800 Unterseen-Interlaken (Bern)
t: 033 822 8716 e: info@lazyrancho.ch
alanrogers.com/CH9430 www.lazyrancho.ch

Accommodation: ☑Pitch ☑Mobile home/chalet ☐ Hotel/B&B ☐ Apartment

This super site is in a quiet location with fantastic views of the dramatic mountains of Eiger, Monch and Jungfrau. Neat, orderly and well maintained, the site is situated in a wide valley just 1 km. from Lake Thun and 1.5 km. from Interlaken. The English speaking owners lovingly care for the site and will endeavour to make you feel very welcome. Connected by gravel roads, the 155 pitches, of which 90 are for touring units, are on well tended level grass (some with hardstanding, all with 10A electricity). There are 28 pitches also with water and waste water drainage. This is a quiet, friendly site, popular with British visitors. The owners offer advice on day trips out, and how to get the best bargains on the railway.

You might like to know

There are many and varied hikes and mountain bike trails available throughout the Jungfrau region.

- ☑ Walking notes or maps available
- ☑ Waymarked footpath – direct access from site
- ☑ Waymarked footpath within 1 km. of site
- ☑ Cycle trail – direct access from site
- ☑ Cycle trail access within 2 km. of site
- ☑ Mountain bike track within 2 km. of site
- ☑ Bicycle hire on site
- ☐ Accompanied hiking trips
- ☐ Accompanied cycling trips
- ☑ Drying room for wet clothes/boots
- ☐ Packed lunch service

Facilities: Two good sanitary blocks are both heated with free hot showers, good facilities for disabled campers and a baby room. Laundry. Campers' kitchen with microwave, cooker, fridge and utensils. Motorcaravan service point. Well stocked shop. TV and games room. Play area. Small swimming pool. Bicycle hire (June-Aug). Free WiFi. Free bus in the Interlaken area – bus stop is five minutes walk from site. Off site: Cycle trails and waymarked footpaths. Riding 500 m. Golf and bicycle hire 1 km. Fishing 1 km. Boat launching 1.5 km. Interlaken 2 km.

Open: 1 May - 20 October.

Directions: Site is on north side of Lake Thun. From road 8 (Thun-Interlaken) on south side of lake take exit 24 Interlaken West. Follow towards lake at roundabout then follow signs for campings. Lazy Rancho is Camp 4. The last 500 m. is a little narrow but no problem. GPS: 46.68605, 7.830633

Charges guide

Per unit incl. 2 persons and electricity	CHF 30,50 - 54,50
extra person	CHF 6,00 - 8,00
child (6-15 yrs)	CHF 3,50 - 4,80
dog	free - CHF 3,00

Payment also accepted in euros.

SWITZERLAND – Lauterbrunnen

Camping Jungfrau

CH-3822 Lauterbrunnen (Bern)
t: 033 856 2010 e: info@camping-jungfrau.ch
alanrogers.com/CH9460 www.camping-jungfrau.ch

Accommodation: ☑Pitch ☑Mobile home/chalet ☐ Hotel/B&B ☐ Apartment

This friendly site has a very imposing and dramatic situation in a steep valley with a fine view of the Jungfrau at the end. It is a popular site and, although you should usually find space, in season do not arrive too late. A fairly extensive area with grass pitches and hardcore access roads. All 391 pitches (250 for touring) have shade in parts, electrical connections (13A) and 50 have water and drainage also. Over 30% of the pitches are taken by seasonal caravans and it is used by two tour operators. Family owned and run by Herr and Frau Fuchs, you can be sure of a warm welcome and English is spoken. You can laze here amid real mountain scenery, though it does lose the sun a little early. There are many active pursuits available in the area, as well as trips on the Jungfrau railway and mountain lifts.

You might like to know

From the local railway station you can get to the Jungfraujoch station with some excellent walking opportunities en-route.

☑ Walking notes or maps available
☑ Waymarked footpath – direct access from site
☐ Waymarked footpath within 1 km. of site
☐ Cycle trail – direct access from site
☑ Cycle trail access within 2 km. of site
☐ Mountain bike track within 2 km. of site
☑ Bicycle hire on site
☐ Accompanied hiking trips
☐ Accompanied cycling trips
☑ Drying room for wet clothes/boots
☐ Packed lunch service

Facilities: Three fully equipped modern sanitary blocks can be heated in winter and one provides facilities for disabled visitors. Baby baths. Laundry facilities. Motorcaravan services. Well equipped campers' kitchen. Excellent shop with photo printing facility. Self-service restaurant with takeaway (May-end Oct). General room with tables and chairs, TV, drink machines, amusements. Playgrounds and covered play area. Excursions and some entertainment in high season. Mountain bike hire. Internet point and WiFi. ATM. Drying room. Ski store. Off site: Free bus to ski station (in winter only).

Open: All year.

Directions: Go through Lauterbrunnen and fork right at far end (look for signpost) before road bends left, 100 m. before church. The final approach is not very wide.
GPS: 46.58807, 7.91077

Charges guide

Per person	CHF 9,80 - 11,90
child (6-15 yrs)	CHF 4,80 - 5,50
pitch incl. electricity (plus meter in winter)	CHF 24,00 - 29,50
dog	CHF 3,00

Camping Eienwäldli

Wasserfallstrasse 108, CH-6390 Engelberg (Unterwalden)
t: 041 637 1949   e: info@eienwaeldli.ch
alanrogers.com/CH9570   www.eienwaeldli.ch

Accommodation: ☑Pitch ☐ Mobile home/chalet   ☑Hotel/B&B   ☐ Apartment

This super site has facilities which must make it one of the best in Switzerland. It is situated in a beautiful location, 3,500 feet above sea level, surrounded by mountains on the edge of the delightful village of Engelberg. Half of the site is taken up by static caravans which are grouped together at one side. The camping area is in two parts – nearest the entrance there are 57 hardstandings for caravans and motorcaravans, all with electricity (metered), and beyond this is a flat meadow for about 70 tents. Reception can be found in the very modern foyer of the Eienwäldli Hotel which also houses the indoor pool, health complex, shop and café/bar. The indoor pool has been most imaginatively rebuilt as a Felsenbad spa bath with adventure pool, steam and relaxing grottoes, Kneipp's cure, children's pool with water slides, solarium, Finnish sauna and eucalyptus steam bath (charged for). Being about 35 km. from Luzern by road and with a rail link, it makes a quiet, peaceful base from which to explore the Vierwaldstattersee region, walk in the mountains or just enjoy the scenery.

You might like to know

A great variety of walks are available in the area, making good use of the excellent mountain railway and cable car network.

- ☑ Walking notes or maps available
- ☑ Waymarked footpath – direct access from site
- ☐ Waymarked footpath within 1 km. of site
- ☐ Cycle trail – direct access from site
- ☑ Cycle trail access within 2 km. of site
- ☑ Mountain bike track within 2 km. of site
- ☐ Bicycle hire on site
- ☑ Accompanied hiking trips
- ☐ Accompanied cycling trips
- ☑ Drying room for wet clothes/boots
- ☐ Packed lunch service

Facilities: The main toilet block, heated in cool weather, is situated at the rear of the hotel and has free hot water in washbasins (in cabins) and (charged) showers. A new modern toilet block has been added near the top end of the site. Washing machines and dryers. Shop. Café/bar. Small lounge. Indoor pool complex. Ski facilities including a drying room. Large play area with a rafting pool fed by fresh water from the mountain stream. Torches useful. TV. WiFi. Golf. Off site: Golf driving range and 18-hole course nearby. Fishing and bicycle hire 1 km. Riding 2 km.

Open: All year.

Directions: From N2 Gotthard motorway, leave at exit 33 Stans-Sud and follow signs to Engelberg. Turn right at T-junction on edge of town and follow signs to 'Wasserfall' and site. GPS: 46.80940, 8.42367

Charges guide

Per person	CHF 6,00 - 9,00
child (6-15 yrs)	CHF 3,00 - 4,50
pitch incl. electricity (plus meter)	CHF 10,00 - 17,00
dog	CHF 1,30 - 2,00

Credit cards accepted (surcharge).

Camping des Glaciers

CH-1944 La Fouly (Valais)
t: **027 783 1826** e: **info@camping-glaciers.ch**
alanrogers.com/CH9660 www.camping-glaciers.ch

Accommodation: ☑Pitch ☑Mobile home/chalet ☐Hotel/B&B ☐Apartment

Camping des Glaciers is set amidst magnificent mountain scenery in a peaceful location in the beautiful Ferret Valley, 1,600 m. above sea level (care is needed with long units). The site offers some pitches in an open, undulating meadow and the rest are level, individual plots of varying sizes in small clearings, between bushes and shrubs or under tall pines. Most of the 220 pitches have 10A electricity. M. Alain Darbellay has now taken over the reins from his mother, who ran the site for 40 years, and he intends to maintain the strong family interest and friendships built up over the years. Additional land has been added to increase the number of pitches available. This is a site for those seeking relaxation in pure, fresh mountain air or boundless opportunities for mountain walking. Marked tracks bring The Grand Saint Bernard Pass and the path around Mont Blanc within range, in addition to many others, with an abundance of flora and fauna for added interest. The local bus links to Orsieres, then trains to the old Roman city of Martigny.

You might like to know

Mountain bike hire is available at a number of locations in Verbier, with miles of trails on offer.

- ☑ Walking notes or maps available
- ☑ Waymarked footpath – direct access from site
- ☐ Waymarked footpath within 1 km. of site
- ☐ Cycle trail – direct access from site
- ☑ Cycle trail access within 2 km. of site
- ☐ Mountain bike track within 2 km. of site
- ☐ Bicycle hire on site
- ☑ Accompanied hiking trips
- ☐ Accompanied cycling trips
- ☑ Drying room for wet clothes/boots
- ☐ Packed lunch service

Facilities: Three sanitary units of exceptional quality are heated when necessary. The newest unit has super facilities for children and wide access for disabled visitors. Hot water is free in all washbasins (some in cabins), showers and sinks. British style WCs. Washing machines and dryers in each block, one block has a drying room, another a baby room. Gas supplies. Motorcaravan services. Small shop. Recreation room with TV. Playground. WiFi (charged). Torches and long leads may be useful. Off site: Adventure park 100 m. Shops and restaurants 500 m. Riding 8 km. Bicycle hire 20 km.

Open: 15 May - 30 September.

Directions: Leave Martigny-Gd St Bernard road (no. 21/E27) to the right where signed Orsieres/La Fouly. Site is signed on right at end of La Fouly village. Take care along narrow access road. GPS: 45.93347, 7.09367

Charges guide

Per unit incl. 2 persons and electricity	CHF 28,40 - 35,50
extra person	CHF 8,00
child (2-12 yrs)	CHF 4,00
dog	CHF 3,00

Camping de Molignon

Route de Molignon, 163, CH-1984 Les Haudères (Valais)
t: 027 283 1240 e: info@molignon.ch
alanrogers.com/CH9670 www.molignon.ch

Accommodation: ☑Pitch ☑Mobile home/chalet ☐ Hotel/B&B ☐ Apartment

Camping de Molignon, surrounded by mountains, is a peaceful haven 1,450 m. above sea level. The rushing stream at the bottom of the site and the sound of cow bells and birdsong are likely to be the only disturbing factors in summer. The 100 pitches for tourists (75 with 10A electricity) are on well tended terraces leading down to the river. Excellent English is spoken by the owner's son who is now running the site. He is always pleased to give information on all that is available from the campsite. The easy uphill drive from Sion in the Rhône Valley is enhanced by ancient villages and the Pyramids of Euseigne. These unusual structures, cut out by erosion from masses of morainic debris, have been saved from destruction by their unstable rocky crowns. Although this is essentially a place for mountain walking (guided tours available), climbing and relaxing, there is a geological museum in Les Haudères, which has links with a British university. Cheese making and interesting flora and fauna add interest for those wishing to explore the area.

You might like to know
Over 100 km. of mountain bike trails (bike hire is available 1 km. from the site).

- ☑ Walking notes or maps available
- ☑ Waymarked footpath – direct access from site
- ☐ Waymarked footpath within 1 km. of site
- ☐ Cycle trail – direct access from site
- ☑ Cycle trail access within 2 km. of site
- ☑ Mountain bike track within 2 km. of site
- ☐ Bicycle hire on site
- ☑ Accompanied hiking trips
- ☐ Accompanied cycling trips
- ☑ Drying room for wet clothes/boots
- ☐ Packed lunch service

Facilities: Two fully equipped sanitary blocks, heated in cool weather, with free hot showers. Baby room. Washing machines and dryer. Kitchen for hikers. Motorcaravan services. Gas supplies. Shop for basic supplies (15/6-15/9). Restaurant. Heated swimming pool with cover for cool weather (6x12 m). Sitting room for games and reading. Playground. Guided walks, climbing, geological museum, winter skiing. Fishing. Off site: Tennis and hang-gliding near. Ski and sports gear hire 1 km. Bicycle hire 1 km. Riding 1.5 km. Langlauf in winter.

Open: All year.

Directions: Leave the motorway at exit 27 and follow signs southwards from Sion for the Val d'Herens through Evolène to Les Haudères where site is signed on the right at the beginning of the village. GPS: 46.09003, 7.50722

Charges guide

Per unit incl. 2 persons and electricity	CHF 28,30 - 34,40
extra person	CHF 5,80 - 7,20
child (4-16 yrs)	CHF 3,20 - 4,00
dog	CHF 2,55 - 3,20

TCS Camping Fontanivas

Via Fontanivas 9, CH-7180 Disentis (Graubünden)
t: 081 947 4422 e: camping.disentis@tcs.ch
alanrogers.com/CH9865 www.campingtcs.ch/disentis

Accommodation: ☑Pitch ☐ Mobile home/chalet ☐ Hotel/B&B ☐ Apartment

Nestled in the Surselva valley with superb views of the surrounding mountains, this is an attractive site with its own lake. Surrounded by tall pine trees, the site is owned by the Touring Club of Switzerland (the Swiss version of the AA) and provides 110 flat, level pitches, 81 with 13A electricity. There are plenty of opportunities for walks, nature trails and cycle rides, whilst the more adventurous can enjoy themselves canyoning, rafting, hang-gliding or mountain biking. For children, the playground is a challenging combination of water, rocks and bridges. Hardy souls can brave the fresh mountain waters of the lake. The Medelser Rhine near Disentis is known to be the richest place in gold in the country. Over the years many people have come to Switzerland to bury or hide their gold, but if you go to Disentis/Müster you have the chance of finding some! Since the 1980s when serious prospecting began there has been a gold rush in Disentis. That apart, this is an ideal holiday spot for both sports fans and nature lovers.

You might like to know

One of the more unusual activities in the area is llama trekking!

- ☑ Walking notes or maps available
- ☑ Waymarked footpath – direct access from site
- ☐ Waymarked footpath within 1 km. of site
- ☐ Cycle trail – direct access from site
- ☑ Cycle trail access within 2 km. of site
- ☑ Mountain bike track within 2 km. of site
- ☐ Bicycle hire on site
- ☐ Accompanied hiking trips
- ☐ Accompanied cycling trips
- ☑ Drying room for wet clothes/boots
- ☐ Packed lunch service

Facilities: The excellent sanitary block is well maintained with free showers and hairdryers. Facilities for disabled visitors. Baby room. Washing machine and dryer. Motorcaravan services. Shop. Restaurant/bar. Play room. Bicycle hire. Fishing. Caravans and tent bungalows to rent. WiFi throughout (charged). Off site: Disentis 2 km. Indoor pool.

Open: 20 April - 23 September.

Directions: The site is 2 km. south of Disentis. From Andermatt take the Oberalppass to Disentis. In town at T-junction turn right towards Lukmanier. Site is at bottom of hill on left, past the droopy power cables. From the East, on arriving in the town, keep left onto Lukmanier Road. GPS: 46.697, 8.85272

Charges guide

Per unit incl. 2 persons and electricity	CHF 36,30 - 44,30
extra person	CHF 7,40 - 9,40
child (6-15 yrs)	CHF 3,70 - 4,70
dog	CHF 3,00 - 5,00

Ferienparadies Natterer See

Natterer See 1, A-6161 Natters (Tirol)
t: 051 254 6732   e: info@natterersee.com
alanrogers.com/AU0060   www.natterersee.com

Accommodation: ☑ Pitch   ☐ Mobile home/chalet   ☐ Hotel/B&B   ☑ Apartment

In a quiet location arranged around two lakes and set amidst beautiful alpine scenery, this site founded in 1930 is renowned as one of Austria's top sites. Over the last few years many improvements have been carried out and pride of place goes to the innovative, award-winning, multifunctional building at the entrance to the site. This contains all of the sanitary facilities expected of a top site, including a special section for children, private bathrooms to rent and also a dog bath. The reception, shop, café/bar/bistro and cinema are on the ground floor, and on the upper floor is a panoramic lounge where the owner has assembled the largest collection of model camping cars and caravans in Europe. Almost all of the 235 pitches are for tourers. They are terraced, set on gravel/grass, all have electricity and most offer a splendid view of the mountains. The site's lakeside restaurant with bar and large terrace has a good menu and is the ideal place to spend the evening. With a bus every hour and the city centre only 19 minutes away this is also a good site from which to visit Innsbruck.

You might like to know

A free shuttle bus is available for some accompanied walks, and hiking boots and day packs are also available for hire.

☑ Walking notes or maps available
☑ Waymarked footpath – direct access from site
☐ Waymarked footpath within 1 km. of site
☑ Cycle trail – direct access from site
☐ Cycle trail access within 2 km. of site
☑ Mountain bike track within 2 km. of site
☑ Bicycle hire on site
☑ Accompanied hiking trips
☑ Accompanied cycling trips
☑ Drying room for wet clothes/boots
☐ Packed lunch service

Facilities: The large sanitary block has underfloor heating, some private cabins, plus excellent facilities for babies, children and disabled visitors. Laundry facilities. Motorcaravan services. Bar. Restaurant and takeaway. Pizzeria. Good shop. Playgrounds. Children's activity programme. Day nursery in high season. Sports field. Archery. Youth room with games, pool and billiards. TV room. Open-air cinema. Mountain bike hire. Aquapark (1/5-30/9). Surf bikes and pedaloes. Canoes and mini sailboats for rent. Fishing. Daily entertainment (mid May-mid Oct). Dogs are not accepted in high season (July/Aug). WiFi (charged). Off site: Riding 6 km. Golf 12 km.

Open: All year.

Directions: From Inntal autobahn (A12) take Brenner autobahn (A13) as far as Innsbruck-sud/Natters exit (no. 3). Turn left by Shell petrol station onto B182 to Natters. At roundabout take first exit and immediately right again and follow signs to site 4 km. Do not use sat nav for final approach to site, follow camping signs. GPS: 47.23755, 11.34201

Charges guide

Per unit incl. 2 persons and electricity	€ 23,40 - € 34,60
extra person	€ 5,90 - € 8,30
child (under 13 yrs)	€ 4,60 - € 6,10

AUSTRIA – Kramsach

Camping Seehof

Reintalersee, Moosen 42, A-6233 Kramsach (Tirol)
t: 053 376 3541 e: info@camping-seehof.com
alanrogers.com/AU0065 www.camping-seehof.com

Accommodation: ☑Pitch ☐ Mobile home/chalet ☐ Hotel/B&B ☑ Apartment

Camping Seehof is a family run site and excellent in every respect. It is situated in a marvellous, sunny and peaceful location on the eastern shores of the Reintalersee lake. The site's comfortable restaurant has a terrace with lake and mountain views and serves local dishes as well as homemade cakes and ice cream. The site is in two areas: a small one next to the lake is ideal for sunbathing, the other larger one adjoins the excellent sanitary block. There are 170 pitches, 130 of which are for touring (20 tent pitches), served by good access roads and with 16A electricity (Europlug) and TV points; 80 pitches are fully serviced. Seehof provides an ideal starting point for walking, cycling and riding (with a riding stable nearby) and skiing in winter. The Alpbachtal Seeland card is available without cost at reception and allows free bus transport and free daily entry to many worthwhile attractions in the region. With easy access from the A12 autobahn the site is also a useful overnight stop.

You might like to know
This is a great site for winter holidays with cross-country skiing adjacent and a free shuttle bus to the slopes.

- ☑ Walking notes or maps available
- ☐ Waymarked footpath – direct access from site
- ☑ Waymarked footpath within 1 km. of site
- ☐ Cycle trail – direct access from site
- ☑ Cycle trail access within 2 km. of site
- ☐ Mountain bike track within 2 km. of site
- ☑ Bicycle hire on site
- ☐ Accompanied hiking trips
- ☐ Accompanied cycling trips
- ☑ Drying room for wet clothes/boots
- ☐ Packed lunch service

Facilities: The sanitary facilities are first class and include ten bathrooms to rent for private use. Baby room. Facilities for disabled visitors. Dog shower. Washing machine and dryer. Ski room. Motorcaravan service point. Small shop. Good restaurant. Bread available each morning from 07.00. Playground. WiFi throughout (charged). Bicycle hire. Fishing. Apartments to rent. Renovated fitness and play rooms.
Off site: Tiroler farmhouse museum 1 km. Kramsach 3 km. Rottenberg 4 km. Swarovski Kristallwelten.

Open: All year.

Directions: From the A12 take Kramsach exit and follow signs for Zu den Seen past Camping Krummsee and northern shore of lake, then right at the crossroads. Camping Seehof (300 m) is the first campsite you reach. Park on left, reception is on the right, follow campsite directions. GPS: 47.46188, 11.90734

Charges guide

Per unit incl. 2 persons and electricity	€ 17,30 - € 26,30
extra person	€ 4,60 - € 6,90
child (2-14 yrs)	€ 3,00 - € 4,50
dog	€ 3,00

AUSTRIA – Prutz

Aktiv-Camping Prutz Tirol

Pontlatzstrasse 22, A-6522 Prutz (Tirol)
t: 054 722 648 e: info@aktiv-camping.at
alanrogers.com/AU0155 www.aktiv-camping.at

Accommodation: ☑Pitch ☐ Mobile home/chalet   ☐ Hotel/B&B   ☐ Apartment

Aktiv-Camping is a long site which lies beside, and is fenced off from, the River Inn. Most of the 100 individual level pitches are for touring and are 80 sq.m. They all have 6A electrical connections and in the larger area fit together sideways and back to back. As a result, the site can sometimes have the appearance of being quite crowded. There is a separate overnight area for motorcaravans. This is an attractive area with many activities in both summer and winter for all age groups. You may well consider using this site not just as an overnight stop, but also for a longer stay. From Roman times onwards, when the Via Augusta passed through, this border region's strategic importance has left behind many fortifications that today feature among its many tourist attractions. Others include rambling, cycling and mountain biking, swimming in lakes and pools as well as interesting, educational and adventurous activities for children. The Tiroler Summer card, available without charge at reception, has free offers and discounts for many attractions; in addition the booklet Wonderful Holiday Bliss, free at reception, contains a wealth of useful tourist information.

You might like to know
The Tirol is known mostly for its wonderful mountain scenery and seemingly unlimited hiking potential. There are plenty of straightforward options for beginners as well as rather more ambitious routes for experts.

- ☑ Walking notes or maps available
- ☐ Waymarked footpath – direct access from site
- ☑ Waymarked footpath within 1 km. of site
- ☐ Cycle trail – direct access from site
- ☑ Cycle trail access within 2 km. of site
- ☑ Mountain bike track within 2 km. of site
- ☐ Bicycle hire on site
- ☑ Accompanied hiking trips
- ☑ Accompanied cycling trips
- ☑ Drying room for wet clothes/boots
- ☐ Packed lunch service

Facilities: The sanitary facilities are of a high standard, with private cabins and good facilities for disabled visitors. Baby room. Washing machine. Dog shower. Small shop (all year). Bar (15/5-15/9). Takeaway (15/5-15/9). Play room. Ski room. Skating rink. Children's entertainment. Guided walks, skiing (free shuttle service). WiFi throughout. Off site: Riding 1 km. Indoor pool at Feichten, Pilgrim's Church at Kaltenbrunn. Kaunertaler Glacier.

Open: All year.

Directions: Travelling west from Innsbruck on the E60/A12 for 65 km. Exit at Landeck and follow the B315 (direction Reschenpass) turn south onto the B180 signed Bregenz, Arlberg, Innsbruck and Fern Pass for 11 km. to Prutz. Site is signed to the right from the B180 over the bridge. GPS: 47.08833, 10.65831

Charges guide

Per unit incl. 2 persons and electricity	€ 16,00 - € 25,90
extra person	€ 4,00 - € 7,20
child (5-14 yrs)	€ 2,50 - € 4,00
dog	€ 2,50 - € 3,50

Sportcamp Woferlgut

Kroessenbach 40, A-5671 Bruck (Salzburg)
t: 065 457 3030 e: info@sportcamp.at
alanrogers.com/AU0180 www.sportcamp.at

Accommodation: ☑Pitch ☑Mobile home/chalet ☑Hotel/B&B ☑Apartment

The village of Bruck lies at the junction of the B311 and the Grossglocknerstrasse in the Hohe Tauern National Park. Sportcamp Woferlgut, a family run site, is one of the best in Austria. Surrounded by mountains, the site is quite flat with pleasant views. The 350 level, grass pitches are marked out by shrubs (300 for touring units) and each has 16A electricity (Europlug), water, drainage, cable TV socket and gas point. A high grass bank separates the site and the road. The site's own lake, used for swimming and fishing, is surrounded by a landscaped sunbathing area. A free activity and entertainment programme is provided all year round. This includes live music evenings, a club for children, weekly barbecues and guided cycle and mountain tours. The fitness centre has a fully equipped gym, whilst another building contains a sauna and cold dip, Turkish bath, solarium (all free), massage (charged), and a bar. In winter, a cross-country skiing trail and toboggan run lead from the site and a free bus service is provided to nearby skiing facilities. With Salzburg to the north and Innsbruck to the northwest, the management is pleased to advise on local attractions and tours.

You might like to know

Free of charge: Spa area with sauna, Turkish bath, cold plunge pool, Kneipp pool, relaxation room and bar, leisure facilities with swimming lake, heated outdoor pool, three tennis courts, beach volleyball, soccer fields and child care (mid-May-September and Christmas).

☑ Walking notes or maps available
☑ Waymarked footpath – direct access from site
☑ Waymarked footpath within 1 km. of site
☑ Cycle trail – direct access from site
☑ Cycle trail access within 2 km. of site
☑ Mountain bike track within 2 km. of site
☑ Bicycle hire on site
☑ Accompanied hiking trips
☑ Accompanied cycling trips
☑ Drying room for wet clothes/boots
☑ Packed lunch service

Facilities: Three modern sanitary blocks (the newest in a class of its own) have excellent facilities, including private cabins, underfloor heating and music. Laundry facilities. Facilities for disabled visitors. Family bathrooms for hire. Motorcaravan services. Shop. Bar, restaurant and takeaway. Small, heated outdoor pool and children's pool (1/5-15/10). Fitness centre. Two playgrounds, indoor play room and children's cinema. Tennis. Bicycle hire. Fishing. Watersports and lake swimming. Collection of small animals with pony rides for young children. New adventure golf course. WiFi throughout (charged). Off site: ATM 500 m. Riding 1.5 km. Golf 3 km. Sailing 3.5 km. Hiking and skiing nearby.

Open: All year.

Directions: Site is southwest of Bruck. From road B311, Bruck bypass, take southern exit (Grossglockner) and site is signed from the junction of B311 and B107 roads (small signs). GPS: 47.2838, 12.81694

Charges guide

Per unit incl. 2 persons and electricity (plus meter)	€ 23,00 - € 32,80
extra person	€ 5,40 - € 8,70
child (2-10 yrs)	€ 4,30 - € 6,40
dog	€ 3,30 - € 4,50

Park Grubhof

Nr. 39, A-5092 Saint Martin bei Lofer (Salzburg)
t: 065 888 237 e: home@grubhof.com
alanrogers.com/AU0265 www.grubhof.com

Accommodation: ☑Pitch ☑Mobile home/chalet ☑Hotel/B&B ☑Apartment

Park Grubhof is a well organised, spacious site in a very scenic riverside location. The 200 pitches all with 12A electricity, have been carefully divided into separate areas for different types of visitor – dog owners, young people, families and groups, and a quiet area. There are 150 very large pitches, all with electricity, water and drainage, along the bank of the Saalach river. Although new, the central building housing reception, a cosy inn, a shop with cafeteria, as well as a super sauna and wellness area and some of the site's sanitary facilities, has been built in traditional Tirolean style using, in part, materials reclaimed from old farmhouses. Some areas are wooded with plenty of shade, others are more open and there are some very attractive log cabins. Many of the activities on offer are based around the river, where you will find barbecue areas, canoeing and white water rafting, fishing and possibly swimming. A cross-county track is 300 m. away and snow cleared winter walks start directly from the site. Bordering the National Park of Berchtesgaden, the area is renowned for hiking, mountain climbing and cycling (the site is on the Tauernradweg cycling trail). Excellent English is spoken.

You might like to know

Walking and cycling at Grubhof offers treks into the Berchtesgaden National Park, flat cycle paths along the river or ambitious MTB tours – everything is on your doorstep. A warm welcome awaits you at this spacious site with large pitches set in spectacular and unspoilt countryside.

☑ Walking notes or maps available
☑ Waymarked footpath – direct access from site
☐ Waymarked footpath within 1 km. of site
☑ Cycle trail – direct access from site
☐ Cycle trail access within 2 km. of site
☑ Mountain bike track within 2 km. of site
☐ Bicycle hire on site
☑ Accompanied hiking trips
☑ Accompanied cycling trips
☑ Drying room for wet clothes/boots
☐ Packed lunch service

Facilities: Two attractive, modern sanitary units built with plenty of glass and wood, give good provision of all facilities. Large showers. Some washbasins in cubicles. Saunas, steam bath, massage, fitness room. Separate facilities for canoeists. Motorcaravan service point. Shop, restaurant and bar. WiFi throughout (charged). Playground. Games room. Children's playroom. Watersports. Bicycle hire. Cabins to rent. Hotel and B&B accommodation. Off site: Cross-country track 300 m. Swimming pools at Lofer 1 km. Skiing at Lofer Alm 2 km. Gorges and caves 5-7 km. Salzburg 40 minutes drive. Many marked walking and cycling trails.

Open: All year excl. November.

Directions: From A12 exit 17 (south of Kufstein) take B178 east to St Johann in Tyrol, then continue on B178 to Lofer, then south on B311 towards Zell am See. Site is 200 m. after Lagerhaus filling station on left.
GPS: 47.57498, 12.70497

Charges guide

Per unit incl. 2 persons and electricity	€ 19,00 - € 31,50
extra person	€ 5,90 - € 7,90
child (under 15 yrs)	€ 3,90 - € 4,90

No credit cards.

FRANCE – Orpierre

Camping des Princes d'Orange

F-05700 Orpierre (Hautes-Alpes)
t: 04 92 66 22 53   e: campingorpierre@wanadoo.fr
alanrogers.com/FR05000   www.campingorpierre.com

Accommodation: ☑Pitch ☑Mobile home/chalet   ☐ Hotel/B&B   ☐ Apartment

This attractive, terraced site, set on a hillside above the village has been thoughtfully developed. Muriel, the owner, speaks excellent English and the genuine, friendly welcome means many families return year upon year, bringing in turn new generations. Divided into five terraces, each with its own toilet block, some of its 100 generously sized pitches (96 for touring) enjoy good shade from trees and have electricity connections (10A). In high season, one terrace is reserved as a one-star camping area for young people. Orpierre has an enchanting maze of medieval streets and houses, almost like a trip back through the centuries. Whether you choose to drive, climb, walk or cycle, there is plenty of wonderful scenery to discover in the immediate vicinity, whilst not far away, some exhilarating hang-gliding and parascending can be enjoyed. It is renowned as a world class rock climbing venue, with over 600 climbing routes in the surrounding mountains. For those seeking to 'get away from it all' in an area of outstanding natural beauty, there can be few more tranquil sites.

You might like to know

There are twice-weekly hikes accompanied by a mid-altitude mountain guide.

☑ Walking notes or maps available
☐ Waymarked footpath – direct access from site
☑ Waymarked footpath within 1 km. of site
☐ Cycle trail – direct access from site
☑ Cycle trail access within 2 km. of site
☑ Mountain bike track within 2 km. of site
☐ Bicycle hire on site
☑ Accompanied hiking trips
☐ Accompanied cycling trips
☐ Drying room for wet clothes/boots
☐ Packed lunch service

Facilities: Six well equipped toilet blocks. Baby bath. Laundry facilities. Bread. Bar (1/4-31/10). Heated swimming pool, paddling pool (15/6-15/9). Play area with inflatable climbing tower. Boules. Games room. Fridge hire. Only gas barbecues are permitted. Free WiFi around reception area. Off site: Orpierre with a few shops and bicycle hire 500 m. Fishing 7 km. Nearest shopping centre Laragne 12 km. Riding 19 km. Hang-gliding. Parascending. Rock climbing. Walking. Mountain biking. Gorges de Guil.

Open: 1 April - 31 October.

Directions: Turn off N75 road at Eyguians onto the D30. Site is signed on left at crossroads in the centre of Orpierre village.
GPS: 44.31121, 5.69677

Charges guide

Per unit incl. 2 persons and electricity	€ 23,00 - € 30,00

No credit cards.

FRANCE – Lagorce

Castel Domaine de Sévenier

Sévenier, F-07150 Lagorce (Ardèche)
t: 04 75 88 29 44 e: domainedesevenier@orange.fr
alanrogers.com/FR07660 www.sevenier.net

Accommodation: ☐ Pitch ☑ Mobile home/chalet ☐ Hotel/B&B ☐ Apartment

Le Domaine de Sévenier is a modern, high quality chalet complex enjoying a hilltop location with fine panoramic views over the surrounding garrigue, a unique mix of oak trees, juniper, rosemary and thyme. Located 4 km. from Vallon-Pont-d'Arc and 800 m. from the pretty village of Lagorce, the domaine is an old winery which has been sensitively converted and offers accommodation in well appointed wooden chalets, serving the needs of different sized families. Rest and relaxation is the theme here and the restaurant has a good reputation. On-site amenities include a swimming pool and a separate children's pool. The site has links to Nature Parc Camping de l'Ardèche and guests are welcome to use the camping site's evening entertainment but there are no touring pitches at Sévenier. The site's restaurant specialises in local cuisine using local organic produce as far as possible, and features a number of fine local wines. Nearby Lagorce maintains its wine production (Côtes du Vivarais is also renowned for its silk culture and its wine production), as well as a delightful botanical footpath.

You might like to know
A footpath to the village of Lagorce (1 km) runs through the site. Vallon Pont d'Arc (4 km) and Ruoms (8 km) are both easily accessible on foot. A hiking map can be purchased in reception.

☑ Walking notes or maps available
☑ Waymarked footpath – direct access from site
☑ Waymarked footpath within 1 km. of site
☑ Cycle trail – direct access from site
☑ Cycle trail access within 2 km. of site
☑ Mountain bike track within 2 km. of site
☑ Bicycle hire on site
☑ Accompanied hiking trips
☐ Accompanied cycling trips
☐ Drying room for wet clothes/boots
☐ Packed lunch service

Facilities: The sanitary block includes hot showers and provision has been made for disabled visitors. Washing machine. Restaurant. Bar. Shop. Outdoor, heated swimming pool. Children's pool. Activity programme. Bicycle hire. Play area. Minigolf. Tourist information. Fully equipped chalets for rent. No touring pitches. Off site: Lagorce 800 m. (shops and cafés). Fishing 4 km. Riding 15 km. Cycle and walking tracks. Riding. Vallon Pont d'Arc 5 km.

Open: 30 March - 4 November.

Directions: Head north from Vallon-Pont-d'Arc (at western end of the Ardèche gorges) on D1 and upon reaching Lagorce, follow signs to the site. GPS: 44.434151, 4.410989

Charges guide

Contact the site for details.

Kawan Village le Coin Tranquille

6 chemin des Vignes, F-38490 Les Abrets (Izère)
t: 04 76 32 13 48   e: contact@coin-tranquille.com
alanrogers.com/FR38010   www.coin-tranquille.com

Accommodation: ☑ Pitch ☑ Mobile home/chalet   ☐ Hotel/B&B   ☐ Apartment

Les Abrets is well placed for visits to the Savoie regions and the Alps. It is an attractive, well maintained site of 192 grass pitches (178 for tourers), all with 6A electricity. They are separated by neat hedges of hydrangea, flowering shrubs and a range of trees to make a lovely environment doubly enhanced by the rural aspect and marvellous views across to the mountains. This is a popular, family run site with friendly staff, making it a wonderful base for exploring the area. Set in the Dauphiny countryside north of Grenoble, Le Coin Tranquille is truly a quiet corner, especially outside school holiday times, although it is still popular with families in high season. The Chartreuse caves near Voiron are well worth a visit, as is the Monastery, and a mountain railway goes to the summit of the Chartreuse Massif.

You might like to know

An accompanied walk is organised by the site's friendly English-speaking owners every Wednesday morning.

☑ Walking notes or maps available
☐ Waymarked footpath – direct access from site
☑ Waymarked footpath within 1 km. of site
☐ Cycle trail – direct access from site
☑ Cycle trail access within 2 km. of site
☐ Mountain bike track within 2 km. of site
☐ Bicycle hire on site
☐ Accompanied hiking trips
☐ Accompanied cycling trips
☐ Drying room for wet clothes/boots
☐ Packed lunch service

Facilities: The central well appointed sanitary block is well kept, heated in low season. Facilities for children and disabled visitors. Two smaller blocks provide facilities in high season. Busy shop. Excellent restaurant. Heated swimming pool and paddling pool (1/5-30/9; no Bermuda style shorts) with sunbathing areas. Play area. TV and games in bar. Quiet reading room. Weekly entertainment for children and adults (July/Aug) including live music (not discos). Bicycle hire (limited). WiFi. Off site: Les Abrets with shops and supermarket 2 km. Riding 6 km. Fishing 8 km.

Open: 1 April - 31 October.

Directions: Les Abrets is 70 km. southeast of Lyon at junction of D1006 (previously N6) and D1075 (previously N75). From roundabout in town take N6 towards Chambéry, turning left in just under 2 km. (signed restaurant and camping). Follow signs along country lane for just over 1 km. and entrance is on right. GPS: 45.54115, 5.60778

Charges guide

Per unit incl. 2 persons and electricity (10A)	€ 18,00 - € 32,00
extra person	€ 4,00 - € 7,50
child (2-7 yrs)	€ 2,50 - € 5,00
dog	€ 1,00

Sunêlia le Col-Vert

Lac de Léon, 1548 route de l'Etang, F-40560 Vielle-Saint-Girons (Landes)
t: 08 90 71 00 01   e: contact@colvert.com
alanrogers.com/FR40050   www.colvert.com

Accommodation: ☑ Pitch ☑ Mobile home/chalet   ☐ Hotel/B&B   ☐ Apartment

This large, well maintained campsite is well laid out on the shores of Lac de Léon and offers 185 mobile homes for rent and 380 touring pitches. The pitches range from simple ones to those with water and a drain, and there are eight with private, well designed, modern sanitary facilities. In low season it is a quiet site and those pitches beside the lake offer a wonderful backdrop to relaxing pastimes. During the main season it is a lively place for children of all ages. A pool complex offers a standard pool for swimming, a pool for children with a water canon and fountains, plenty of sun beds and a heated indoor pool. Swimming is also permitted in the lake alongside the many water-based activities. A fitness and beauty spa offers a wide range of treatments. This extensive but natural site edges a nature reserve and stretches along the Lac de Léon, a conservation area, for 1 km. on a narrow frontage. This makes it particularly suitable for those who want to practice watersports such as sailing and windsurfing. An overall charge is made for some but not all of the leisure activities.

You might like to know

Bicycle hire is available on site. There are miles of cycle tracks leading through the vast forests of Les Landes, including access to the region's superb beaches.

☑ Walking notes or maps available
☑ Waymarked footpath – direct access from site
☑ Waymarked footpath within 1 km. of site
☑ Cycle trail – direct access from site
☐ Cycle trail access within 2 km. of site
☑ Mountain bike track within 2 km. of site
☑ Bicycle hire on site
☑ Accompanied hiking trips
☑ Accompanied cycling trips
☐ Drying room for wet clothes/boots
☑ Packed lunch service

Facilities: Four toilet blocks, one heated. One block with fun facilities for children based on Disney characters. Facilities for disabled guests. Laundry facilities. Motorcaravan services. Shops, bar/restaurant, takeaway (13/4-8/9). Swimming pool complex with three pools (all season). Spa, fitness centre and sauna. Play area. Games room. Sports areas. Boules. Tennis. Bicycle hire. Minigolf. Fishing. Riding. Sailing school (15/6-15/9). Communal barbecues. WiFi (charged). Off site: Walking and cycle ways in the forest. Atlantic beaches 5 km. Golf 10 km.

Open: 13 April - 22 September.

Directions: Site is off D652 Mimizan-Léon road, 4 km. south of crossroads with D42 at St Girons. The road to the lake and the site is signed at Vielle. GPS: 43.90285, -1.3125

Charges guide

Per unit incl. 2 persons and electricity	€ 17,40 - € 44,60
extra person	€ 2,20 - € 7,10
child (3-12 yrs)	€ 1,70 - € 6,10
dog	€ 1,20 - € 4,50

FRANCE – Moliets-Plage

Le Saint-Martin Camping

Avenue de l'Océan, F-40660 Moliets-Plage (Landes)
t: 05 58 48 52 30   e: contact@camping-saint-martin.fr
alanrogers.com/FR40190   www.camping-saint-martin.fr

Accommodation: ☑Pitch ☑Mobile home/chalet   ☐ Hotel/B&B   ☐ Apartment

A family site aimed mainly at couples and young families, le Saint-Martin is a welcome change from most of the sites in this area in that it has only a relatively small number of mobile homes (127) compared to the number of touring pitches (383). First impressions are of a neat, tidy, well cared for site and the direct access to a wonderful fine sandy beach is an added bonus. The pitches are mainly typically French in style with low hedges separating them, and with some shade. Electricity hook ups are 10/15A and a number of pitches also have water and drainage. Entertainment in high season is low key (with the emphasis on quiet nights) – daytime competitions and a miniclub, plus the occasional evening entertainment, well away from the pitches and with no discos or karaoke. With pleasant chalets and mobile homes to rent, a top-class pool complex and an 18-hole golf course 700 m. away (special rates negotiated), this would be an ideal destination for a golfing weekend or longer stay.

You might like to know

Courant d'Huchet, a conservation area, is delightful and has a number of walks and some beautiful views.

☑ Walking notes or maps available
☐ Waymarked footpath – direct access from site
☑ Waymarked footpath within 1 km. of site
☑ Cycle trail – direct access from site
☐ Cycle trail access within 2 km. of site
☐ Mountain bike track within 2 km. of site
☑ Bicycle hire on site
☑ Accompanied hiking trips
☑ Accompanied cycling trips
☑ Drying room for wet clothes/boots
☐ Packed lunch service

Facilities: Seven toilet blocks of a high standard and very well maintained, have washbasins in cabins, large showers, baby rooms and facilities for disabled visitors. Motorcaravan service point. Washing machines and dryers. Fridge rental. Supermarket. Bars, restaurants and takeaways. Indoor pool, jacuzzi and sauna (charged July/Aug). Outdoor pool area with jacuzzi and paddling pool (15/6-15/9). Multisport pitch. Play area. Bicycle hire. Beach access. Internet access. Electric barbecues only. Off site: Fishing and beach 300 m. Golf and tennis 700 m. Sailing 6 km. Riding 8 km.

Open: 4 April - 7 November.

Directions: From the N10 take D142 to Lèon, then D652 to Moliets-et-Mar. Follow signs to Moliets-Plage, site is well signed.
GPS: 43.85242, -1.38732

Charges guide

Per unit incl. 2 persons and electricity	€ 22,70 - € 48,60
extra person	€ 6,00 - € 8,50
child (under 13 yrs)	€ 4,00 - € 6,00
dog	free - € 5,00

Prices are for reserved pitches.

Leading Camping les Alicourts

Domaine des Alicourts, F-41300 Pierrefitte-sur-Sauldre (Loir-et-Cher)
t: 02 54 88 63 34 e: info@lesalicourts.com
alanrogers.com/FR41030 www.lesalicourts.com

Accommodation: ☑Pitch ☑Mobile home/chalet ☐ Hotel/B&B ☐ Apartment

A secluded holiday village set in the heart of the forest, with many sporting facilities and a super spa centre, Camping les Alicourts is midway between Orléans and Bourges, to the east of the A71. There are 490 pitches, 150 for touring and the remainder occupied by mobile homes and chalets. All pitches have electricity connections (6A) and good provision for water, and most are 150 sq.m. (min. 100 sq.m.). Locations vary, from wooded to more open areas, thus giving a choice of amount of shade. All facilities are open all season and the leisure amenities are exceptional. The Senseo Balnéo centre offers indoor pools, hydrotherapy, massage and spa treatments for over 18s only (some special family sessions are provided). An inviting outdoor water complex (all season) includes two swimming pools, a pool with wave machine and a beach area, not forgetting three water slides. Competitions and activities are organised for adults and children, including a high season club for children with an entertainer twice a day, a disco once a week and a dance for adults. A member of Leading Campings Group.

You might like to know

The site is part of the Loire à Vélo programme.

☑ Walking notes or maps available
☐ Waymarked footpath – direct access from site
☑ Waymarked footpath within 1 km. of site
☐ Cycle trail – direct access from site
☐ Cycle trail access within 2 km. of site
☑ Mountain bike track within 2 km. of site
☑ Bicycle hire on site
☐ Accompanied hiking trips
☐ Accompanied cycling trips
☐ Drying room for wet clothes/boots
☑ Packed lunch service

Facilities: Three modern sanitary blocks include some washbasins in cabins and baby bathrooms. Laundry facilities. Facilities for disabled visitors. Motorcaravan services. Shop. Restaurant. Takeaway in bar with terrace. Pool complex. Spa centre. 7-hectare lake (fishing, bathing, canoes, pedaloes, cable-ski). 9-hole golf course. Adventure play area. Tennis. Minigolf. Boules. Roller skating/skateboarding (bring own equipment). Bicycle hire. Internet access and WiFi (charged).

Open: 27 April - 7 September.

Directions: From A71, take Lamotte-Beuvron exit (no 3) or from N20 Orléans to Vierzon turn left on to D923 towards Aubigny. After 14 km. turn right at camping sign on to D24E. Site signed in 2 km. GPS: 47.54398, 2.19193

Charges guide

Per unit incl. 2 persons	
and electricity	€ 20,00 - € 46,00
extra person	€ 7,00 - € 10,00
child (1-17 yrs acc. to age)	free - € 9,00
dog	€ 5,00 - € 7,00

Reductions for low season longer stays.

Camping la Grande Sologne

Rue des Peupliers, F-41600 Nouan-le-Fuzelier (Loir-et-Cher)
t: 02 54 88 70 22   e: info@campinggrandesologne.com
alanrogers.com/FR41180   www.campinggrandesologne.com

Accommodation: ☑Pitch   ☑Mobile home/chalet   ☐ Hotel/B&B   ☐ Apartment

The enthusiastic new managers, who speak many languages, are working hard to raise this site to a high standard. It is in a parkland setting on the southern edge of Nouan-le-Fuzelier close to the A71 autoroute, making this an ideal spot to spend some time relaxing whilst en route north or south. It has 165 spacious, level, grass pitches with a variety of mature trees giving some shade, with 150 for touring. All have electricity, but long leads may be necessary. They are marked but not delineated, although some hedges are being planted. Access is easy for large outfits. The site is entered through a very attractive park which has some interesting sculptures and houses the excellent municipal pool and tennis courts, which are free to campers. The interesting village of Nouan-le-Fuzelier is only 400 m. and well worth exploring. There are nearly 3,000 lakes in this fascinating area and several interesting historical market towns. Several of the famous châteaux, such as Chambord, are an easy drive.

You might like to know

The Sologne area is a paradise for walkers. Just 1 km. from the campsite, you can explore the local fauna and the flora at Le Domaine des Levrys, a fantastic wooded area of 230 hectares and a wildlife hub.

☑ **Walking notes or maps available**
☐ **Waymarked footpath – direct access from site**
☑ **Waymarked footpath within 1 km. of site**
☐ **Cycle trail – direct access from site**
☑ **Cycle trail access within 2 km. of site**
☐ **Mountain bike track within 2 km. of site**
☐ **Bicycle hire on site**
☐ **Accompanied hiking trips**
☐ **Accompanied cycling trips**
☐ **Drying room for wet clothes/boots**
☐ **Packed lunch service**

Facilities: Three modern toilet blocks with all necessary facilities including those for campers with disabilities. Washing machine, dryer. Snack bar (July/Aug). Small shop (all season). Games/TV room. Motorcaravan services. Fishing. Bicycle hire. Play area. WiFi. Off site: Municipal swimming pool, tennis courts, adjacent (free). Many interesting old market towns and villages within easy reach. Famous equestrian centre 7 km. Chambord and other famous châteaux. Lakes for fishing.

Open: 1 April - 15 October.

Directions: Nouan-le-Fuzelier is between exits 3 and 4 on A71 autoroute, south of Orléans. Take D2020 to site at southern edge of Nouan-le-Fuzelier, opposite railway station. Well signed. GPS: 47.533863, 2.037674

Charges guide

Per unit incl. 2 persons and electricity	€ 18,00 - € 22,00
extra person	€ 4,50 - € 5,50
child (1-17 yrs acc. to age)	€ 3,40
dog	€ 1,00

Kawan Village du Deffay

B.P. 18 Le Deffay, Sainte Reine-de-Bretagne, F-44160 Pontchâteau (Loire-Atlantique)
t: 02 40 88 00 57   e: campingdudeffay@wanadoo.fr
alanrogers.com/FR44090   www.camping-le-deffay.com

Accommodation: ☑Pitch ☑Mobile home/chalet ☑Hotel/B&B ☐ Apartment

A family managed site, Château du Deffay is a refreshing departure from the usual formula in that it is not over organised or supervised and has no tour operator units. The 170 good sized, fairly level pitches have pleasant views and are either on open grass, on shallow terraces divided by hedges, or informally arranged in a central, slightly sloping wooded area. Most have electricity (6/10A). The bar, restaurant and covered pool are located within the old courtyard area of the smaller château that dates from before 1400. A significant attraction of the site is the large, unfenced lake which is well stocked for fishermen and even has free pedaloes for children. The landscape is wonderfully natural and the site blends well with the rural environment of the estate, lake and farmland which surround it. Alpine type chalets overlook the lake and fit in well with the environment and the larger château (built 1880 and which now offers B&B) stands slightly away from the camping area but provides a wonderful backdrop for an evening stroll. The site is close to the Brière Regional Park, the Guérande Peninsula, and La Baule and is just 20 minutes drive from the nearest beach.

Facilities: The main toilet block is well maintained, if a little dated, and is well equipped including washbasins in cabins, provision for disabled visitors, and a baby bathroom. Laundry facilities. Shop. Bar and small restaurant with takeaway (1/5-15/9). Covered and heated swimming pool (at 28 degrees when we visited) and paddling pool (all season). Play area. TV. Entertainment in season including miniclub. Fishing and pedalos on the lake. Torches useful. WiFi (charged). Off site: Golf 7 km. Riding 10 km. Beach 25 km.

Open: 1 May - 30 September.

Directions: Site is signed from D33 Pontchâteau-Herbignac road near Ste Reine. Also signed from the D773 and N165-E60 (exit 13). GPS: 47.44106, -2.15981

Charges guide

Per unit incl. 2 persons and electricity	€ 19,55 - € 29,69
extra person	€ 3,43 - € 5,74
child (2-12 yrs)	€ 2,35 - € 4,00

You might like to know

Why not take part in one of the themed treks (nature, trees etc) through the beautiful local countryside?

- ☑ Walking notes or maps available
- ☑ Waymarked footpath – direct access from site
- ☑ Waymarked footpath within 1 km. of site
- ☐ Cycle trail – direct access from site
- ☐ Cycle trail access within 2 km. of site
- ☐ Mountain bike track within 2 km. of site
- ☑ Bicycle hire on site
- ☐ Accompanied hiking trips
- ☐ Accompanied cycling trips
- ☐ Drying room for wet clothes/boots
- ☐ Packed lunch service

Kawan Village les Bois du Bardelet

Route de Bourges, le Petit Bardelet, F-45500 Gien (Loiret)
t: 02 38 67 47 39 e: contact@bardelet.com
alanrogers.com/FR45010 www.bardelet.com

Accommodation: ☑Pitch ☑Mobile home/chalet ☐ Hotel/B&B ☐ Apartment

This attractive, high quality site, ideal for families with young children, is in a rural setting and well situated for exploring the less well known eastern part of the Loire Valley. Two lakes (one for boating, one for fishing) and a pool complex have been attractively landscaped in 18 hectares of former farmland, blending old and new with natural wooded areas and more open grassland with rural views. There are 245 large, level grass pitches with 120 for touring units. All have at least 10A electricity, 15 have water, waste water and 16A electricity, and some 30 have hardstanding. Eight have individual en-suite sanitary units beside the pitch. Converted former farm buildings house a bar and an excellent restaurant with a covered terrace overlooking a small lake. There is an impressive range of leisure facilities including an indoor pool with jacuzzi, a new wellness suite with hot tub and sauna, and an imaginative heated indoor water play area for children. A daily or weekly family club card can be purchased (€5/day) to make use of any of the charged activities (tennis, fishing, canoeing, pétanque, minigolf, table tennis). Excursions are organised to châteaux and vineyards, plus several riverboat trips.

You might like to know

Just 5 km. from the River Loire, the site is part of the Loire à Vélo programme. The knowledgeable and friendly team in reception will be pleased to help you make the most of the Loire Valley by bike.

☑ Walking notes or maps available
☐ Waymarked footpath – direct access from site
☐ Waymarked footpath within 1 km. of site
☐ Cycle trail – direct access from site
☑ Cycle trail access within 2 km. of site
☐ Mountain bike track within 2 km. of site
☑ Bicycle hire on site
☐ Accompanied hiking trips
☐ Accompanied cycling trips
☐ Drying room for wet clothes/boots
☐ Packed lunch service

Facilities: Two heated toilet blocks (effectively unisex, one open in high season only) have some washbasins in cubicles, controllable showers, an en-suite unit for disabled visitors and a baby room. Washing machines and dryers. Minimart, bar, takeaway and restaurant (all 1/5-15/9). Heated outdoor pool (1/5-31/8). Heated indoor pool and children's pool. Wellness centre with sauna, hot-tub, Shiatsu massage and beauty treatments. Fitness and jacuzzi rooms. Beach on lake. Games area. Canoeing and fishing. Tennis. Minigolf. Volleyball. Pétanque. Children's playground with trampoline. Kids' Club, sports tournaments, excursions and activities, aquagym, archery (July/Aug). Bicycle hire. Chalets/mobile homes for hire. Free WiFi in bar area. Off site: Supermarket 5 km. Riding 6 km.

Open: 19 April - 30 September.

Directions: Site is 7 km. south of Gien. Leave A77 autoroute, exit 19 and take D940 (Bourges) to bypass Gien. Continue on D940 for 5 km. At junction with D53 (no left turn) turn right and right again to cross D940. Follow signs to site. GPS: 47.64152, 2.61528

Charges guide

Per unit incl. 2 persons and electricity	€ 20,10 - € 33,50
extra person (over 2 yrs)	€ 5,20 - € 6,90

Camping Touristique de Gien

Rue des Iris, F-45500 Poilly-lez-Gien (Loiret)
t: 02 38 67 12 50 e: camping-gien@wanadoo.fr
alanrogers.com/FR45030 www.camping-gien.com

Accommodation: ☑Pitch ☑Mobile home/chalet ☐ Hotel/B&B ☐ Apartment

This open, attractive, well cared for site lies on a bank of the Loire with views of the town of Gien and its château. It has a long river frontage, which includes a good expanse of sandy beach. There are 200 good sized, level, grassy pitches with 150 for touring. All have 10A electricity. Some are shaded by mature trees and many have good views over the river. The bar and restaurant, with a pleasant outdoor area, are open to the public and meals are reasonably priced. Soirées with different themes are held weekly in July and August. The town of Gien, with its shops, bars, restaurants and château, is within a kilometre just across the bridge. A long distance cycle path passes the entrance. This is an excellent base for exploring the eastern end of the Loire valley, and Gien has a festival celebrating the heritage of this part of the Loire at Ascensiontide. The tourist office organises a wide range of activities both sporting and cultural. There is a regular bus service to Orléans, an ancient city well known for its association with Joan of Arc.

You might like to know

Gien can be found at the crossroads of the Sologne, the Berry and the Gâtinais, with the Sancerre region close at hand. There are miles of great cycle tracks to explore the region's riches.

- ☑ Walking notes or maps available
- ☐ Waymarked footpath – direct access from site
- ☑ Waymarked footpath within 1 km. of site
- ☑ Cycle trail – direct access from site
- ☐ Cycle trail access within 2 km. of site
- ☐ Mountain bike track within 2 km. of site
- ☑ Bicycle hire on site
- ☐ Accompanied hiking trips
- ☐ Accompanied cycling trips
- ☐ Drying room for wet clothes/boots
- ☑ Packed lunch service

Facilities: Two unisex toilet blocks, one heated, are fairly basic but clean and have washbasins in cabins, controllable showers and facilities for disabled visitors. Laundry. Bar and restaurant (1/5-30/9), both open to the public. Shop 50 m. outside gates (closed Sun. outside July/Aug). Inflatable swimming pool (with removable roof) and paddling pools (15/5-15/9). Play area. Games area. Outdoor exercise equipment. Minigolf. Bicycle and pedal cart hire. Canoe hire. Fishing. Sandy beach. Some organised activities (July/Aug). WiFi over site (charged).
Off site: Children's club on beach. Town less than 1 km. Hypermarket 1.5 km. Riding 2 km.

Open: First weekend in March - All Saints' in November.

Directions: Gien is 70 km. southeast of Orléans. Leave A77 at exit 19 and take D940 (Bourges) to bypass Gien to east; cross Loire and turn north at roundabout towards town centre. At traffic lights before bridge, turn west to Poilly-lez-Gien and site is on right in 800 m.
GPS: 47.68229, 2.62315

Charges guide

Per unit incl. 2 persons and electricity	€ 20,00
extra person	€ 6,00
child (under 12 yrs)	€ 4,00

Camping Soleil du Pibeste

16 avenue du Lavedan, F-65400 Agos-Vidalos (Hautes-Pyrénées)
t: 05 62 97 53 23 e: info@campingpibeste.com
alanrogers.com/FR65090 www.campingpibeste.com

Accommodation: ☑Pitch ☑Mobile home/chalet ☐ Hotel/B&B ☐ Apartment

The Dusserm family, the owners, are very proud of their regional culture and heritage and will ensure you are made welcome. The reception is friendly, with an area for local foods, maps and good tourist information. This site is special because of the range and type of activities that it offers. These include tai chi, qi gong, massage, archery, walking, climbing and canoeing. Choral and creative activities are offered. There are 38 touring pitches all with 3-15A electricity. Mobile homes and chalets are available to rent. The mountain view from the terrace is magnificent. Ongoing improvements include a second swimming pool incorporating facilities for campers with disabilities. Play areas are being expanded to cater for different age groups, including lively teenagers. There is a shop and bread can be ordered for delivery the following morning. The bar and restaurant area is large and well equipped. The site is rural but has a bus stop just outside providing access to Argelès-Gazost and the renowned pilgrimage town of Lourdes. The family also offers a pick up service from various airports and towns.

You might like to know

The friendly campsite owners know the Pyrénées very well and organise accompanied walks for all abilities.

- ☑ Walking notes or maps available
- ☐ Waymarked footpath – direct access from site
- ☑ Waymarked footpath within 1 km. of site
- ☐ Cycle trail – direct access from site
- ☑ Cycle trail access within 2 km. of site
- ☐ Mountain bike track within 2 km. of site
- ☐ Bicycle hire on site
- ☑ Accompanied hiking trips
- ☐ Accompanied cycling trips
- ☐ Drying room for wet clothes/boots
- ☐ Packed lunch service

Facilities: Two heated toilet blocks. Baby room. Facilities for disabled visitors (key). Cleaning can be variable. Washing machine, dryer. Motorcaravan services. Bar, snack bar, restaurant and pizzeria (June-Sept). Shop for essentials. Bread can be ordered for next day delivery. Swimming pool with panoramic views and loungers (June-Sept). New children's play areas (4-6 yrs and 6-10 yrs). Multisports pitch. Volleyball. Tennis. Badminton. Bowling. Basketball. 4 free activities weekly (tai chi, qi gong, rollerblading, archery, etc; July/Aug). Entertainment programme, children's activities and craft workshops (July/Aug). Massage (charged). Library. WiFi (charged). Off site: Fishing 800 m. Rafting 2 km. Golf 10 km. Riding 15 km. Skiing 20 km.

Open: 1 May - 30 September.

Directions: Agos Vidalos is on the N21, which becomes the D821, 5 km. south of Lourdes. Leave expressway at second exit, signed Agos Vidalos and continue on D921B to site, a short distance on the right. GPS: 43.03557, -0.07093

Charges guide

Per unit incl. 2 persons and electricity	€ 23,00 - € 36,00
extra person	€ 8,00
dog	€ 5,00

Domaine le Jardin du Marais

208 route de Saint-Gilles, F-85300 Le Perrier (Vendée)
t: **02 51 68 09 17** e: **info@lejardindumarais.eu**
alanrogers.com/FR85635 www.lejardindumarais.eu

Accommodation: ☑Pitch ☑Mobile home/chalet ☐ Hotel/B&B ☐ Apartment

A delightful, family campsite situated, as its name suggests, in a country setting on the edge of the marshes. It is beautifully kept and has excellent facilities including a well stocked shop, a pleasant bar/restaurant and a good pool complex. The enthusiastic and hardworking owners are keen to welcome more British visitors who will be sure of a warm reception. Of the 120 pitches, 52 are available for touring: the established pitches offer some shade and have electricity and water nearby; a new area offers large pitches with electricity, water and drainage, but bushes and trees have yet to mature. The beaches are just seven kilometres away. For shops, bars and restaurants you can use the nearby village of Le Perrier or head for the resorts of Saint Jean-de-Monts or Saint Hilaire-de-Riez where there are also large supermarkets and frequent markets. Just south of Saint Hilaire is the busy fishing port and resort of Saint Gilles Croix-de-Vie where you can have a drink or a meal on the quayside, wander along the pedestrianised shopping streets or admire the yachts in the thriving marina.

You might like to know
Saint Jean-de-Monts has recently opened an excellent 26 km. cycle track which runs close to the coast.

☑ Walking notes or maps available
☐ Waymarked footpath – direct access from site
☑ Waymarked footpath within 1 km. of site
☐ Cycle trail – direct access from site
☑ Cycle trail access within 2 km. of site
☐ Mountain bike track within 2 km. of site
☑ Bicycle hire on site
☐ Accompanied hiking trips
☐ Accompanied cycling trips
☐ Drying room for wet clothes/boots
☐ Packed lunch service

Facilities: Two bright, modern sanitary blocks provide hot showers and washbasins in cubicles. Baby bath and changing. En-suite facility for disabled visitors. Washing machine and dryer. Chemical disposal and motorcaravan services arranged. Shop, bar/restaurant and takeaway (all season, on demand). Outdoor pool with paddling pool (15/6-15/9). Indoor heated pool (15/4-15/9). Solarium. Fitness room. Play area. Fishing on small lake (fenced and gated). Children's club, daytime activities and evening entertainment (July/Aug). Games area. TV. Bicycle hire. Internet point. WiFi (charged) in bar area. Off site: Riding 4 km. Beach and sailing 7 km. Golf 8 km.

Open: 1 April - 2 October.

Directions: Le Perrier is 51 km. northwest of La Roche-sur-Yon and 11 km. southwest of Challans. Site is 2 km. to south on D59 to Le Pissot and St Gilles; from the new route of the D753 Challans-St Jean-de-Monts road turn south on D59 and site is on right in 300 m. GPS: 46.80133, -1.980656

Charges guide

Per unit incl. 2 persons and electricity	€ 18,00 - € 31,00
extra person	€ 5,00 - € 7,50
child (2-11 yrs)	€ 3,00 - € 6,00

South Penquite Farm

South Penquite, Blisland, Bodmin PL30 4LH (Cornwall)
t: **01208 850491** e: **thefarm@bodminmoor.co.uk**
alanrogers.com/UK0302 www.southpenquite.co.uk

Accommodation: ☑Pitch ☑Mobile home/chalet ☐ Hotel/B&B ☐ Apartment

South Penquite offers real camping with no frills. It is set on a 200-hectare hill farm, high on Bodmin Moor between the villages of Blisland and St Breward. The farm achieved organic status in 2001 and runs a flock of 300 ewes and a herd of 40 cattle and horses. The camping is small scale and intended to have a low impact on the surrounding environment. Fifty tents or simple motorcaravans (no caravans) can pitch around the edge of three walled fields, roughly cut in the midst of the moor. You can find shelter or a view. Four yurts are available to rent in one field, complete with wood burning stoves – quite original. Campfires are permitted with wood available from the farmhouse.
You will also find horses, ponies, chickens, geese, ducks and turkeys which show their approval (or not) by the skin around their necks changing colour! A walk of some two miles takes you over most of the farm and some of the moor, taking in a Bronze Age hut settlement, the river and a standing stone. It is also possible to fish for brown trout on the farm's stretch of the De Lank river, a tributary of the Camel.

You might like to know

South Penquite Farm runs a number of Bushcraft days during the summer holidays. These family days are an introduction to bushcraft and nature awareness skills, learning about the local wildlife and the environment in a fun and engaging way.

- ☑ Walking notes or maps available
- ☑ Waymarked footpath – direct access from site
- ☐ Waymarked footpath within 1 km. of site
- ☐ Cycle trail – direct access from site
- ☑ Cycle trail access within 2 km. of site
- ☐ Mountain bike track within 2 km. of site
- ☐ Bicycle hire on site
- ☐ Accompanied hiking trips
- ☐ Accompanied cycling trips
- ☐ Drying room for wet clothes/boots
- ☐ Packed lunch service

Facilities: A smart new pine clad toilet block, with a separate provision of four family-sized showers, with solar heated rainwater. Washing machine and dryer. Small fridge and freezer. Home produced lamb, burgers and sausages available. LPG gas. Facilities for field studies and opportunities for educational groups and schools to learn about the local environment. Bushcraft days. Fishing (requires an EA rod licence and tokens available from the West Country Rivers Trust). Dogs are not accepted. Off site: Riding and cycling 1 mile. Pubs 1.5 and 2.5 miles. Sustrans Route 3 passes close by. North and south coasts within easy reach.

Open: 1 May - 1 November.

Directions: On A30 Bodmin Moor pass Jamaica Inn and sign for Colliford Lake and watch for St Breward sign (to right) immediately at end of dual carriageway. Follow narrow road over moor for 2 miles ignoring any turns, including right turn to St Breward just before South Penquite sign. Follow track over stone bridge through farm gate, then bear left to camping fields. Book in at Farm House. GPS: 50.5445, -4.671833

Charges guide

Per person	£ 7,00 - £ 8,00
child (5-15 yrs)	£ 3,50 - £ 4,00

No credit cards.

Stowford Farm Meadows

Berry Down, Combe Martin, Ilfracombe EX34 0PW (Devon)
t: **01271 882476** e: **enquiries@stowford.co.uk**
alanrogers.com/UK0690 www.stowford.co.uk

Accommodation: ☑ Pitch ☑ Mobile home/chalet ☐ Hotel/B&B ☐ Apartment

Stowford Farm is a friendly, family park set in 500 acres of the rolling North Devon countryside, available for recreation and walking, yet within easy reach of five local beaches. The touring park and its facilities have been developed in the fields and farm buildings surrounding the attractive old farmhouse and provide a village like centre with a comfortable, spacious feel. There are 710 pitches on five slightly sloping meadows separated by Devon hedges of beech and ash. The numbered and marked pitches, some with hardstanding, are accessed by hard roads, most have 10/16A electricity and there are well placed water points. Stowford also provides plenty to keep the whole family occupied without leaving the park, including woodland walks and horse riding from the park's own stables. The Old Stable Bar offers entertainment in high season including barn dances, discos, karaoke and other musical evenings. There is also much for children to do, from the indoor heated pool and under-cover mini zoo where they can handle many sorts of animals (on payment), to the wide range of organised activities on offer. It is also a good base for exploring the North Devon coast and Exmoor.

You might like to know

Seventy acres of woodland has been left for site users' enjoyment and education, and provides an excellent network of waymarked paths and tracks leading deep into the beautiful wooded Bittadon Valley.

☑ Walking notes or maps available
☑ Waymarked footpath – direct access from site
☐ Waymarked footpath within 1 km. of site
☐ Cycle trail – direct access from site
☑ Cycle trail access within 2 km. of site
☐ Mountain bike track within 2 km. of site
☐ Bicycle hire on site
☐ Accompanied hiking trips
☐ Accompanied cycling trips
☐ Drying room for wet clothes/boots
☐ Packed lunch service

Facilities: Five toilet blocks, each looked after by resident wardens, provide good, functional facilities, each block with laundry facilities. The newest block (in field 5) has under-floor heating and includes facilities for disabled visitors. Private family washrooms. Shop. Good value takeaway with restaurant area. Bars and entertainment in season. Indoor pool (22x10 m; heated Easter-Oct) at a small charge. Riding. 18-hole pitch and putt. Crazy golf. 'Kiddies kar' track (all charged). Games room. Large play area. Games and activities organised in high season. WiFi. ATM. Woodland walks. Max. 2 dogs (in separate areas). Caravan centre. Rallies accepted. New development of 40 holiday lodges.
Off site: Fishing 4 miles. Bicycle hire 10 miles.

Open: All year.

Directions: From Barnstaple take A39 towards Lynton. After 1 mile turn left on B3230. Turn right at garage on A3123 and park is 1.5 miles on the right. GPS: 51.174983, -4.05475

Charges guide

Per unit incl. 2 persons and electricity	£ 8,90 - £ 25,70
extra person	free - £ 4,50
child (5-12 yrs)	free - £ 2,50
dog	£ 1,70 - £ 2,70

Rivendale Caravan & Leisure Park

Buxton Road, Alsop-en-le-Dale, Ashbourne DE6 1QU (Derbyshire)
t: **01335 310311** e: **enquiries@rivendalecaravanpark.co.uk**
alanrogers.com/UK3850 www.rivendalecaravanpark.co.uk

Accommodation: ☑Pitch ☑Mobile home/chalet ☑Hotel/B&B ☐ Apartment

This unusual park has been developed in the bowl of a hill quarry which was last worked over 50 years ago. The steep quarry walls shelter three sides with marvellous views over the Peak District National Park countryside to the south. Near the entrance to the park is a renovated stone building which houses reception, shop, bar and a café/restaurant. Nearby are 136 level and landscaped pitches, mostly of a generous size with 16A electricity and a mix of hardstanding and grass. In two separate fields and a copse there is provision for 50 tents and that area includes a fishing lake. All the touring pitches are within easy reach of the central stone-built toilet block which is in keeping with the environment and provided with underfloor heating. A new lodge-style heated toilet block is at the entrance to the tent fields. For rent on the park are B&B rooms, camping pods, lodges and yurts. The park takes up about 11 acres and a further 26 acres belong to the owners, with certain parts suitable for walking. The park is situated almost on the Tissington Trail for walking or off-road cycling and links with the High Peak and Monsal Dale trails. Other walks and cycle rides run along the Manifold, Wye and Dove valleys.

You might like to know
There is an extensive network of cycle routes and footpaths leading straight from Rivendale through spectacular Peakland scenery (www.visitpeakdistrict.com/cycleroutes – routes 7 and 8). Park Rangers provide accompanied walks and there are several bicycle hire centres nearby.

☑ Walking notes or maps available
☑ Waymarked footpath – direct access from site
☐ Waymarked footpath within 1 km. of site
☑ Cycle trail – direct access from site
☐ Cycle trail access within 2 km. of site
☐ Mountain bike track within 2 km. of site
☐ Bicycle hire on site
☐ Accompanied hiking trips
☐ Accompanied cycling trips
☐ Drying room for wet clothes/boots
☑ Packed lunch service

Facilities: Good toilet facilities include some washbasins in cubicles for ladies, and an excellent en-suite room for disabled visitors. Laundry room. Shop. Bar (evenings) and café with home-made and local food (open mornings, lunch and evenings, with limited opening in low season). Packed lunches from reception. Special events monthly and games in main season. Hot tubs for hire, delivered to your pitch. Fly fishing lake. WiFi in some areas (charged). For rent on the park are B&B rooms, camping pods, lodges and yurts. Off site: Bicycle hire nearby. Riding 5 miles. Sailing and boat launching 8 miles. Golf 10 miles. Alton Towers 35 minutes drive.

Open: 1 February - 5 January.

Directions: Park is 7 miles north of Ashbourne on the A515 to Buxton, on the eastern side of the road. It is well signed between the turnings east to Alsop Moor and Matlock (A5012), but take care as this is a very fast section of the A515. GPS: 53.106383, -1.760567

Charges guide

Per unit incl. 2 persons	
and electricity	£ 18,50 - £ 24,00
extra person	£ 2,50
child (4-15 yrs)	£ 2,00
dog	£ 2,00

Castlerigg Hall Touring Park

Castlerigg Hall, Keswick CA12 4TE (Cumbria)
t: **01768 774499** e: **info@castlerigg.co.uk**
alanrogers.com/UK5660 www.castlerigg.co.uk

Accommodation: ☑Pitch ☑Mobile home/chalet ☐ Hotel/B&B ☐ Apartment

This well laid out park was started in the late 1950s by the Jackson family, who over the years have developed and improved the site whilst maintaining its character. Good use has been made of the traditional stone buildings to house the reception and shop, whilst another building houses a modern amenity block along with a really excellent campers' kitchen. Tarmac roads wend their way around the site to the separate tent area of 110 pitches. Gently sloping with some shelter, these pitches have fine views across Keswick, Derwentwater and the western Fells. The 45 caravan pitches tend to be on terraces, again overlooking the lake. Each terrace has a maximum of eight pitches, all on hardstanding and with 10A electricity and nearly all with a water tap and grey water drain. Places to visit include Keswick (about 20 minutes walk), Derwentwater, Ullswater, Penrith, Carlisle, Hadrian's Wall, Rhegad (the village in the hill) and, quite close to the site, Castlerigg stone circle which is believed to be some 4,000 years old, and of course as much walking as you might want. The Jacksons are committed to conservation.

You might like to know

The park is only a 45 minute walk from the summit of Walla Crag, regarded as one of the best viewpoints in England. Whinlatter Forest Cycle trails are accessible by a bike bus, with various grades of trail available. The mysterious, 4,000-year-old Castlerigg Stone Circle is 2 km. from the park, a pleasant 35 minute walk. The Castlerigg Gallery has just been opened displaying stunning landscape photography of the local area.

☑ Walking notes or maps available
☑ Waymarked footpath – direct access from site
☑ Waymarked footpath within 1 km. of site
☐ Cycle trail – direct access from site
☑ Cycle trail access within 2 km. of site
☑ Mountain bike track within 2 km. of site
☐ Bicycle hire on site
☐ Accompanied hiking trips
☐ Accompanied cycling trips
☑ Drying room for wet clothes/boots
☐ Packed lunch service

Facilities: The main toilet block is beautifully fitted out, fully tiled and heated, with showers, vanity style washbasins (2 in cabins) and hair care areas. Unit for disabled visitors (key). Baby area. Fully equipped laundry. Games room and campers' kitchen complete with microwave, toasters, kettle and hot plates. Two other toilet blocks are older in style but newly decorated and clean. Reception houses tourist information and a well stocked shop (with gas). WiFi over part of site. Off site: Hotel/pub for meals adjacent to site. Fishing, golf, riding, bicycle hire and boat launching, all 2 km.

Open: 11 March - 7 November.

Directions: From Penrith take A66 towards Keswick and Cockermouth. Leave at first sign for Keswick (A591) and follow to junction (A5271). Turn left on A591 signed Windermere and after 1 mile, take small road on right signed Castlerigg and Rakefoot. Park entrance is on right after 400 yds. GPS: 54.5931, -3.112583

Charges guide

Per unit incl. 2 persons	
and electricity	£ 19,50 - £ 29,00
extra person (over 4 yrs)	£ 3,50 - £ 5,00
tent per adult	£ 6,95 - £ 8,90
dog	£ 1,60 - £ 2,40

Pen-y-Bont Touring Park

Llangynog Road, Bala LL23 7PH (Gwynedd)
t: **01678 520549** e: **penybont-bala@btconnect.co.uk**
alanrogers.com/UK6340 www.penybont-bala.co.uk

Accommodation: ☑Pitch ☑Mobile home/chalet ☐ Hotel/B&B ☐ Apartment

This is a pretty little park with 59 touring pitches, 47 of which have hardstanding. Connected by circular gravel roads, they are intermingled with trees and tall trees edge the site. Electricity connections (16A) are available, including 11 for tents, and there are 28 serviced pitches with hardstanding, electricity, water and drainage. There are also pitches for 25 seasonal units. The park entrance and the stone building that houses reception and the well stocked shop provide quite a smart image. With views of the Berwyn mountains, Pen-y-bont has a peaceful, attractive and useful location being the closest park to Bala town. Bala Lake is 100 yards and the park is three miles from the Welsh National White Water Centre, with Snowdonia on hand.

You might like to know

There is an excellent walk from the site, leading above Bala to get a great view of Wales' largest natural lake.

☑ Walking notes or maps available
☑ Waymarked footpath – direct access from site
☐ Waymarked footpath within 1 km. of site
☐ Cycle trail – direct access from site
☑ Cycle trail access within 2 km. of site
☑ Mountain bike track within 2 km. of site
☐ Bicycle hire on site
☐ Accompanied hiking trips
☐ Accompanied cycling trips
☐ Drying room for wet clothes/boots
☐ Packed lunch service

Facilities: The toilet block includes washbasins in cubicles and spacious hot showers. Two new cubicles with washbasin and WC. Separate laundry room and an en-suite unit for disabled visitors, that doubles as a baby room, operated by key (£5 deposit). Outside covered area with fencing and concrete floor for dishwashing sinks and bins. Motorcaravan service point. Shop. Bicycle hire. Caravan storage. WiFi (charged). Off site: Fishing 200 yds. Boat launching, golf and riding 2 miles. Monday market in Bala.

Open: 15 March - 27 October.

Directions: Park is 0.5 miles southeast of Bala village on the B4391. Bala is between Dolgellau and Corwen on the A494.
GPS: 52.901717, -3.590117

Charges guide

Per unit incl. 2 persons and electricity	£ 19,00 - £ 23,00
tent pitch incl. 2 persons	£ 15,50 - £ 20,50
extra person	£ 7,50
child (4-16 yrs)	£ 4,00
dog	£ 1,00

Hoddom Castle Caravan Park

Hoddom, Lockerbie DG11 1AS (Dumfries and Galloway)
t: **01576 300251** e: **hoddomcastle@aol.com**
alanrogers.com/UK6910 www.hoddomcastle.co.uk

Accommodation: ☑Pitch ☑Mobile home/chalet ☐ Hotel/B&B ☐ Apartment

The park around Hoddom Castle is landscaped, spacious and well laid out on mainly sloping ground with many mature and beautiful trees, originally part of an arboretum. The drive to the site is just under a mile long with a one way system. Many of the 120 numbered pitches have good views of the castle and have gravel hardstanding with grass for awnings. Most have 16A electrical connections. In front of the castle are flat fields used for tents and caravans with a limited number of electricity hook-ups. The oldest part of Hoddom Castle itself is a 16th-century Borders Pele Tower, or fortified Keep. This was extended to form a residence for a Lancashire cotton magnate, became a youth hostel and was then taken over by the army during WW2. Since then parts have been demolished but the original Border Keep still survives, unfortunately in a semi-derelict state. The park's nine-hole golf course is in an attractive setting alongside the Annan river, where fishing is possible for salmon and trout (tickets available). Coarse fishing is also possible elsewhere on the estate. This is a peaceful base from which to explore historic southwest Scotland.

You might like to know

In the woods surrounding the site there is a mountain bike trail on which anyone can test their off-road skills. The track is about half a mile long and twists and turns through thick bushes and trees.

☑ Walking notes or maps available
☐ Waymarked footpath – direct access from site
☑ Waymarked footpath within 1 km. of site
☐ Cycle trail – direct access from site
☑ Cycle trail access within 2 km. of site
☑ Mountain bike track within 2 km. of site
☐ Bicycle hire on site
☐ Accompanied hiking trips
☐ Accompanied cycling trips
☐ Drying room for wet clothes/boots
☐ Packed lunch service

Facilities: The main toilet block can be heated and is very well appointed. Washbasins in cubicles, 3 en-suite cubicles with WC and basin (one with baby facilities) and an en-suite shower unit for disabled visitors. Two further tiled blocks, kept very clean, provide washbasins and WCs only. Well equipped laundry room at the castle. Motorcaravan service point. Licensed shop at reception (gas available). Bar, restaurant and takeaway (restricted opening outside high season). Games room. Large, grass play area. Crazy golf. Mountain bike trail. Fishing. Golf. Guided walks (high season). Caravan storage. Off site: Tennis nearby.

Open: 1 April - 30 October.

Directions: Leave A74M at exit 19 (Ecclefechan) and follow signs to park. Leave A75 at Annan junction (west end of Annan bypass) and follow signs. GPS: 55.041367, -3.311

Charges guide

Per unit incl. 2 persons	£ 11,50 - £ 18,50
incl. electricity	£ 14,50 - £ 21,50
extra person	£ 3,00
child (7-16 yrs)	£ 1,50

Loch Ken Holiday Park

Parton, Castle Douglas DG7 3NE (Dumfries and Galloway)
t: **01644 470282** e: **office@lochkenholidaypark.co.uk**
alanrogers.com/UK6940 www.lochkenholidaypark.co.uk

Accommodation: ☑Pitch ☑Mobile home/chalet ☐ Hotel/B&B ☐ Apartment

Loch Ken Holiday Park sits right on the shore of the loch, adjacent to the RSPB bird reserve and the Galloway Forest Park – it is a peaceful haven in an Area of Outstanding Natural Beauty. This is a family owned park with 40 touring pitches and 33 caravan holiday homes, ten of which are for rent. The touring pitches, all with 10A electricity, are quite separate and are arranged in a mostly open plan way on a large, neatly mown grass area beside the water. Some of this area is gently undulating. Mature trees border the park and provide an area for walking dogs. Site lighting is minimal so torches are advised. The spacious reception and well stocked shop are centrally located with a separate, well presented tourist information area. There are facilities for launching small boats, but these must be registered with the local council (at reception). This park is probably mostly suited to couples and families with older children who enjoy outdoor pursuits.

You might like to know

The 7 Stanes are seven mountain biking trail centres spanning the south of Scotland, most within easy access of the site, and offering some of the country's best mountain biking.

☑ Walking notes or maps available
☐ Waymarked footpath – direct access from site
☐ Waymarked footpath within 1 km. of site
☐ Cycle trail – direct access from site
☐ Cycle trail access within 2 km. of site
☐ Mountain bike track within 2 km. of site
☐ Bicycle hire on site
☐ Accompanied hiking trips
☐ Accompanied cycling trips
☐ Drying room for wet clothes/boots
☐ Packed lunch service

Facilities: The toilet block has been completely refurbished to modern standards and was exceptionally clean when we visited. Separate facilities in a modern Portacabin unit are provided in the tent area. Facilities for disabled visitors. Gas supplies. Well stocked shop. Good play area. Bicycles, canoes and dinghies for hire. Boat launching (permit from reception). Fishing (permit). Off site: Buses stop at the entrance, but are limited. Skiing 0.5 miles. Golf and riding 7 miles. Bars and restaurants in Castle Douglas 9 miles. Kirkcudbright 15 miles.

Open: 1 March - 31 October.

Directions: From Castle Douglas take the A713 north for 7 miles. Site entrance is on left in Parton. GPS: 55.0104, -4.05568

Charges guide

Per unit incl. 2 persons, 2 children under 10 yrs and electricity	£ 17,00 - £ 22,00
tent, no electricity	£ 12,00 - £ 17,00
extra person	£ 2,00
dog	£ 2,00

Brighouse Bay Holiday Park

Brighouse Bay, Borgue, Kirkcudbright DG6 4TS (Dumfries and Galloway)
t: **01557 870267**   e: **info@gillespie-leisure.co.uk**
alanrogers.com/UK6950   www.brighouse-bay.co.uk

Accommodation: ☑Pitch ☑Mobile home/chalet ☐ Hotel/B&B ☑ Apartment

Hidden away within 1,200 exclusive acres, on a quiet, unspoilt peninsula, this spacious family park is only some 200 yards through bluebell woods from an open, sandy bay. It has exceptional all weather facilities, as well as golf and pony trekking. Over 90 percent of the 210 touring caravan pitches have 10/16A electricity, some with hardstanding and some with water, drainage and TV aerial. The three tent areas are on fairly flat, undulating ground and some pitches have electricity. There are 120 self-contained holiday caravans and lodges of which about 30 are let, the rest privately owned. On site leisure facilities include a golf and leisure club with 16.5 m. pool, water features, jacuzzi, steam room, fitness room, games room (all on payment), golf driving range, bowling green and clubhouse bar and bistro. The 18-hole golf course extends onto the headland with superb views over the Irish Sea to the Isle of Man and Cumbria. The TRSS Approved Pony Trekking Centre offers treks for complete beginners and a range of hacks for the more experienced. Also available are riding lessons and stable management sessions. This well run park is a member of the Best of British group.

You might like to know
The Southern Upland Way is Scotland's longest walk, stretching 212 miles between Portpatrick and Cocksburnpath, and is easily accessed from the site.

- ☑ Walking notes or maps available
- ☐ Waymarked footpath – direct access from site
- ☑ Waymarked footpath within 1 km. of site
- ☐ Cycle trail – direct access from site
- ☑ Cycle trail access within 2 km. of site
- ☑ Mountain bike track within 2 km. of site
- ☐ Bicycle hire on site
- ☐ Accompanied hiking trips
- ☐ Accompanied cycling trips
- ☐ Drying room for wet clothes/boots
- ☐ Packed lunch service

Facilities: The large, well maintained main toilet block includes 10 unisex cabins with shower, basin and WC, and 12 with washbasin and WC. A second, excellent block next to the tent areas has en-suite shower rooms (one for disabled visitors) and bathroom, separate washing cubicles, showers and baby room. Laundry facilities. Motorcaravan service point. Gas supplies. Licensed shop. Bar, restaurant and takeaway. Golf and Leisure Club with indoor pool. Play area. Pony trekking. Quad bikes, boating pond, 10-pin bowling, playgrounds, putting. Nature trails. Coarse fishing. Sea angling and an all-tide slipway for boating enthusiasts. Caravan storage. Tourist information. Leisure facility bookings.

Open: All year.

Directions: In Kirkcudbright turn onto A755 and cross river bridge. In 400 yds. turn left onto B727 at international camping sign. Or follow Brighouse Bay signs off A75 just east of Gatehouse of Fleet. GPS: 54.7875, -4.1291

Charges guide

Per unit incl. 2 persons and electricity	£ 19,50 - £ 26,00
extra person	£ 3,00
child (4-15 yrs)	£ 2,00

The River Tilt Park

Golf Course Road, Blair Atholl, Pitlochry PH18 5TB (Perth and Kinross)
t: 01796 481467   e: stuart@rivertilt.co.uk
alanrogers.com/UK7295   www.rivertiltpark.co.uk

Accommodation: ☑ Pitch   ☑ Mobile home/chalet   ☐ Hotel/B&B   ☐ Apartment

This good quality, family owned park is set on the banks of the River Tilt, a short walk from the village of Blair Atholl, where the 16th-century Blair Castle stands proud. There are 54 privately owned caravan holiday homes. Two central areas have been set aside for touring caravans, motorcaravans and tents, with 31 pitches mostly with hardstanding. Divided by mature shrubs and hedges, all have 10A electricity connections, 18 have water and a drain. One of the areas is reserved for dog owners and their pets. The Steadings Spa provides an indoor pool, solarium, steam room, spa pool and multigym, plus Waves hair salon. Also open to the public, there are charges for these facilities. The park also has an award winning restaurant. Adjacent are a riverside walk and a golf course. There may be some noise from the railway line that runs alongside the park.

You might like to know

The local area proudly boasts many places of natural beauty - many easily accessible on foot. The Falls Of Bruar, Glen Tilt and The Pass of Killicrankie are all manageable walks, attracting visitors of all ages.

☑ Walking notes or maps available
☐ Waymarked footpath – direct access from site
☑ Waymarked footpath within 1 km. of site
☐ Cycle trail – direct access from site
☑ Cycle trail access within 2 km. of site
☑ Mountain bike track within 2 km. of site
☐ Bicycle hire on site
☐ Accompanied hiking trips
☐ Accompanied cycling trips
☐ Drying room for wet clothes/boots
☐ Packed lunch service

Facilities: The purpose built toilet block is centrally situated (with key entry) and provides en-suite toilet and washbasin cabins and individual large preset showers, one suitable for disabled visitors. Baby facilities. Well equipped laundry. Motorcaravan service point. Bar and restaurant. Leisure spa complex with indoor pool, etc. Hair salon. Tennis. WiFi throughout (free). Max. 2 dogs per pitch. Off site: Private fishing and golf adjacent. Bicycle hire 0.5 miles. Riding 1.5 miles. Pitlochry with its famous salmon leap 6 miles. Bus or train from Blair Atholl.

Open: Two weeks after Easter - 10 November.

Directions: From the A9 just north of Pitlochry, take B8079 into Blair Atholl and follow signs for River Tilt. GPS: 56.76538, -3.83962

Charges guide

Per unit incl. 2 persons and electricity	£ 16,00 - £ 20,00
extra person	£ 1,50
child	£ 1,00
dog	£ 2,00

Tummel Valley Holiday Park

Tummel Bridge, Pitlochry PH16 5SA (Perth and Kinross)
t: 01882 634221   e: enquiries@parkdeanholidays.co.uk
alanrogers.com/UK7305   www.parkdeanholidays.co.uk

Accommodation: ☑Pitch ☑Mobile home/chalet ☐ Hotel/B&B ☐ Apartment

Set in the Tay Forest Park on the banks of the River Tummel, this large family holiday park is part of the Parkdean Group. Divided into two areas by the roadway, the main emphasis is on chalets to let on the side that overlooks the river. Privately owned caravan holiday homes and touring pitches are on the other, quieter side. The 26 touring pitches, open plan with hardstanding, electricity hook-up and a shared water point, overlook a small fishing lake, which is an added attraction for all the family. On arrival, you should turn right and park, then cross back to book in. The leisure complex with indoor and outdoor activities is on the river side, as is the reception office.

You might like to know

There are wonderful cycling and walking opportunities here. many are challenging but there is an easy route around picturesque Loch Rannoch, perfect for all abilities and especially families.

- ☑ Walking notes or maps available
- ☐ Waymarked footpath – direct access from site
- ☑ Waymarked footpath within 1 km. of site
- ☐ Cycle trail – direct access from site
- ☑ Cycle trail access within 2 km. of site
- ☐ Mountain bike track within 2 km. of site
- ☐ Bicycle hire on site
- ☐ Accompanied hiking trips
- ☐ Accompanied cycling trips
- ☐ Drying room for wet clothes/boots
- ☐ Packed lunch service

Facilities: The very clean toilet block (recently refurbished) has vanity style washbasins, preset showers and a bathroom in each section. Good facilities for disabled visitors. Well equipped laundry. Chemical disposal but no motorcaravan service point. Shop. Riverside entertainment complex with bar and terrace, restaurant and takeaway. Indoor heated pool and toddlers' splash pool. Solarium and sauna. Amusements. Separate area with pool tables. All weather sports court. Adventure play area. Crazy golf. Nature trails. Bicycle hire. Fishing. Note: all venues are non-smoking. Max. 2 dogs per unit. Off site: Golf and riding 10 miles. Buses leave near park entrance.

Open: Late March/Easter - 31 October.

Directions: Travel through Pitlochry. After 2 miles turn left on B8019 to Tummel Bridge (10 miles). Park is on both the left and right. Touring units should turn right and park, then return to reception on the left. GPS: 56.70742, -4.02002

Charges guide

Per unit incl. 4 persons and electricity	£ 13,00 - £ 32,00
dog	£ 2,00 - £ 3,00

Glen Nevis Touring Park

Glen Nevis, Fort William PH33 6SX (Highland)
t: **01397 702191**   e: **camping@glen-nevis.co.uk**
alanrogers.com/UK7830   www.glen-nevis.co.uk

Accommodation: ☑Pitch ☑Mobile home/chalet ☐ Hotel/B&B ☑ Apartment

Just outside Fort William, in a most attractive and quiet situation with views of Ben Nevis, this spacious park is used by those on active pursuits as well as sightseeing tourists. It comprises eight quite spacious fields, divided between caravans, motorcaravans and tents (steel pegs required). It is licensed for 250 touring caravans but with no specific tent limits. The large touring pitches, many with hardstanding, are marked with wooden fence dividers, 174 with 13A electricity and 100 also have water and drainage. The park becomes full in the peak months but there are vacancies each day. If reception is closed (possible in low season) you site yourself. There are regular security patrols at night in busy periods. The park's own modern restaurant and bar with good value bar meals is a short stroll from the park, open to all. A well managed park with bustling, but pleasing ambiance, watched over by Ben Nevis. Around 1,000 acres of the Glen Nevis estate are open to campers to see the wildlife and explore this lovely area.

You might like to know

The Caledonian Canal is easily accessible by cycle and is an amazing Victorian engineering feat which took 20 years to build and finally connected one coast of Scotland to the other.

☑ **Walking notes or maps available**
☐ **Waymarked footpath – direct access from site**
☑ **Waymarked footpath within 1 km. of site**
☐ **Cycle trail – direct access from site**
☑ **Cycle trail access within 2 km. of site**
☑ **Mountain bike track within 2 km. of site**
☐ **Bicycle hire on site**
☐ **Accompanied hiking trips**
☐ **Accompanied cycling trips**
☐ **Drying room for wet clothes/boots**
☐ **Packed lunch service**

Facilities: The four modern toilet blocks with showers (extra showers in two blocks); and units for visitors with disabilities. An excellent block in Nevis Park (one of the eight camping fields) has some washbasins in cubicles, showers, further facilities for disabled visitors, a second large laundry room and dishwashing sinks. Motorcaravan service point. Shop (Easter-mid Oct), barbecue area and snack bar (May-mid Sept). Play area on bark. Off site: Pony trekking, golf and fishing nearby.

Open: 15 March - 31 October.

Directions: Turn off A82 to east at roundabout just north of Fort William following camp sign. GPS: 56.804517, -5.073917

Charges guide

Per unit incl. 2 persons and electricity	£ 15,20 - £ 22,30
extra person	£ 1,80 - £ 3,20
child (5-15 yrs)	£ 1,00 - £ 1,60
dog	free

Ballinacourty House Touring Park

Glen of Aherlow, Tipperary (Co. Tipperary)
t: 062 565 59 e: info@camping.ie
alanrogers.com/IR9370 www.camping.ie

Accommodation: ☑Pitch ☐ Mobile home/chalet ☑Hotel/B&B ☑Apartment

Ballinacourty House and its cobble-stoned courtyard form the centrepiece of this south facing park with views of the Galtee Mountains. Accessed by a tree-lined lane, the reception area is in part of the renovated 18th-century building, as is the adjoining restaurant. The park is level with 26 touring pitches with 6A electricity and 19 grassy pitches for tents. Some areas are shaded and there are open spaces to accommodate rallies and larger groups. Self-catering cottages and B&B are also available. This tranquil site is very appealing to families with young children. It is an excellent base from which to tour the Rock of Cashel, the Mitchelstown Caves, Swiss Cottage and the towns of Tipperary, Cahir and Cashel. The management has recently begun to keep farm animals in an enclosed part of the park and intends to enhance the estate's entire old walled garden. Activities in the area include horse riding and trekking, fishing for perch and brown trout, cycling, forest walks, three 18-hole golf courses, leisure centre with swimming pool, cinema, theatre and pottery shop.

Facilities: Sanitary facilities provide free hot water and showers. Baby room. Laundry with ironing facilities. Campers' kitchen. Ice pack freezing. Licensed restaurant (early booking advised). Motorcaravan services. Gas supplies. Frisbee golf. TV and games rooms. Picnic benches. Tennis. Play area. Off site: Riding, fishing, golf within 5 miles.

Open: Easter - last Sunday in September.

Directions: Follow the N24 from Tipperary or Cahir to Bansha. Turn on to R663 for 11 km, passing Glen Hotel after 10 km. Follow signs for Ballinacourty House. GPS: 52.41614, -8.21047

Charges guide

Per unit incl. 2 persons and electricity	€ 24,00 - € 27,00
extra person	€ 5,00
child	€ 4,00

You might like to know

The Glen of Aherlow is a walkers' paradise offering a variety of low level loop and mountain walks. Walking and trekking holidays are now the most popular activities in the area, and what better way to enjoy the natural resources of mountains, rivers, lakes, forests and scenic landscape.

- ☑ Walking notes or maps available
- ☐ Waymarked footpath – direct access from site
- ☑ Waymarked footpath within 1 km. of site
- ☐ Cycle trail – direct access from site
- ☑ Cycle trail access within 2 km. of site
- ☐ Mountain bike track within 2 km. of site
- ☐ Bicycle hire on site
- ☐ Accompanied hiking trips
- ☐ Accompanied cycling trips
- ☐ Drying room for wet clothes/boots
- ☐ Packed lunch service

The Apple Touring Park

Moorstown, Cahir (Co. Tipperary)
t: 052 744 1459   e: con@theapplefarm.com
alanrogers.com/IR9410   www.theapplefarm.com

Accommodation: ☑ Pitch ☐ Mobile home/chalet ☐ Hotel/B&B ☐ Apartment

This fruit farm and campsite combination offers an idyllic country holiday venue in one of the most delightful situations imaginable. For touring units only, it is located off the N24, midway between Clonmel and Cahir. The park has 32 pitches in a secluded situation behind the barns; they are mostly grass with 14 hardstandings and 25 electricity connections (13A, Europlug). Entrance is by way of a 300 m. drive flanked by the orchard fields and various non-fruit tree species, which are named and of interest to guests who are free to spend time walking the paths around the farm. When we visited, strawberries were being gathered – the best we had tasted all season – and award-winning apple juice, cordials, jams, etc. are also sold by Con and Noreen in the farm shop. Reception is housed with the other site facilities in a large farmyard barn. Although a rather unusual arrangement, it is central and effective. The towns of Cahir and Clonmel are of historic interest and the countryside around boasts rivers, mountains, Celtic culture and scenic drives.

You might like to know

There are a number of superb excursions on foot, or by bicycle. These include the 15th-century Moorstown Castle (3 km) and the 12th-century Cahir Castle (7 km).

☑ Walking notes or maps available
☐ Waymarked footpath – direct access from site
☑ Waymarked footpath within 1 km. of site
☐ Cycle trail – direct access from site
☑ Cycle trail access within 2 km. of site
☑ Mountain bike track within 2 km. of site
☐ Bicycle hire on site
☐ Accompanied hiking trips
☐ Accompanied cycling trips
☐ Drying room for wet clothes/boots
☐ Packed lunch service

Facilities: Toilet facilities, kept very clean, quite modern in design and with heating, comprise showers, washbasins with mirrors, electric points, etc. in functional units occupying two corners of the large floor space. Facilities for disabled visitors. Also in the barn are dishwashing sinks, washing machine and a fridge/freezer for campers to use. Good drive-on motorcaravan service point. Good tennis court (free). Play area. Dogs are not accepted. WiFi (free). Off site: Fishing, golf, and riding 6 km. Bicycle hire 9 km.

Open: 1 May - 30 September.

Directions: Park is 300 m. off main N24, 9.6 km. west of Clonmel, 6.4 km. east of Cahir. GPS: 52.37663, -7.84262

Charges guide

Per unit incl. 2 persons and electricity	€ 15,50
extra person	€ 6,50
child	€ 4,50

Less 20% for groups of 4 or more.

Wave Crest Touring Park

Caherdaniel (Co. Kerry)
t: 066 947 5188 e: wavecrest@eircom.net
alanrogers.com/IR9560 www.wavecrestcamping.com

Accommodation: ☑Pitch ☐ Mobile home/chalet ☐ Hotel/B&B ☐ Apartment

It would be difficult to imagine a more dramatic location than Wave Crest's on the Ring of Kerry coast. Huge boulders and rocky outcrops tumble from the park entrance on the N70 down to the seashore which forms the most southern promontory on the Ring of Kerry. There are spectacular southward views from the park across Kenmare Bay to the Beara peninsula. Sheltering on grass patches in small coves that nestle between the rocks and shrubbery, are 65 hardstanding pitches and 20 on grass offering seclusion. Electricity connections are available (13A). This park would suit older people looking for a quiet, relaxed atmosphere. A unique feature is the TV room, an old stone farm building with a thatched roof. Its comfortable interior includes a stone fireplace heated by a converted cast iron marker buoy. Caherdaniel is known for its cheerful little pubs and distinguished restaurant. The Derrynane National Park Nature Reserve is only a few kilometres away, as is Derrynane Cove and Bay.

You might like to know
There are some fine local walks with commanding views of beaches, coves and distant mountains. You may catch a view of basking sharks and dolphins.

- ☑ Walking notes or maps available
- ☐ Waymarked footpath – direct access from site
- ☑ Waymarked footpath within 1 km. of site
- ☐ Cycle trail – direct access from site
- ☑ Cycle trail access within 2 km. of site
- ☐ Mountain bike track within 2 km. of site
- ☐ Bicycle hire on site
- ☐ Accompanied hiking trips
- ☐ Accompanied cycling trips
- ☐ Drying room for wet clothes/boots
- ☐ Packed lunch service

Facilities: Two blocks house the sanitary and laundry facilities and include hot showers on payment (€ 1). Small shop and takeaway service (June-Sept). Small play area. Fishing and boat launching. Off site: Riding 1 km. Bicycle hire and golf 10 km. Small beach near and Derrynane Hotel with bar and restaurant.

Open: All year.

Directions: On the N70 (Ring of Kerry), 1.5 km. east of Caherdaniel. GPS: 51.75881, -10.09112

Charges guide

Per unit incl. 2 persons and electricity	€ 27,00
extra person	€ 6,00
child	€ 2,00

Fossa Caravan & Camping Park

Fossa, Killarney (Co. Kerry)
t: 064 663 1497   e: fossaholidays@eircom.net
alanrogers.com/IR9590   www.fossacampingkillarney.com

Accommodation: ☑Pitch ☑Mobile home/chalet ☐ Hotel/B&B ☑Apartment

This park is in the village of Fossa, ten minutes by car or bus (six per day) from Killarney town centre. Fossa Caravan Park has a distinctive reception building and hostel accommodation, a stimulating play area and shop. The park is divided in two – the touring caravan area lies to the right, tucked behind the main building and to the left is an open grass area mainly for campers. Touring pitches, with 10/15A electricity and drainage, have hardstanding and are angled between shrubs and trees in a garden setting. To the rear at a higher level and discreetly placed are 30 caravan holiday homes, sheltered by the thick foliage of the wooded slopes which climb high behind the park. Not only is Fossa convenient for Killarney (5.5 km), it is also en-route for the famed Ring of Kerry, and makes an ideal base for walkers and golfers. Less than eight kilometres away are the famous walk up the Gap of Dunloe, and Carrantuohill, the highest mountain in Ireland.

You might like to know

Fossa is located on the Kerry Way. Killarney National Park, Gap of Dunloe, MacGillycuddy Reeks are all within easy distance of the site.

- ☑ Walking notes or maps available
- ☐ Waymarked footpath – direct access from site
- ☑ Waymarked footpath within 1 km. of site
- ☐ Cycle trail – direct access from site
- ☑ Cycle trail access within 2 km. of site
- ☐ Mountain bike track within 2 km. of site
- ☐ Bicycle hire on site
- ☐ Accompanied hiking trips
- ☐ Accompanied cycling trips
- ☐ Drying room for wet clothes/boots
- ☐ Packed lunch service

Facilities: Modern toilet facilities include showers on payment. En-suite unit for campers with disabilities. Laundry room. Campers' kitchen. Shop. Takeaway (8/7-25/8). TV lounge. Tennis. Play area. Picnic area. Games room. Security patrol. Off site: Fishing and golf 2 km. Riding 3 km. Bicycle hire 5 km. Woodland walk into Killarney. A visit to Killarney National Park is highly recommended.

Open: 1 April - 30 September.

Directions: Approaching Killarney from all directions, follow signs for N72 Ring of Kerry and Killorglin. At last roundabout join R562/N72. Continue for 5.5 km. and Fossa is the second park to the right. GPS: 52.07071, -9.58573

Charges guide

Per unit incl. 2 persons and electricity	€ 22,00 - € 26,00
extra person	€ 6,00
child (under 16 yrs)	€ 2,50
hiker/cyclist incl. tent	€ 8,00 - € 9,00

Mannix Point Touring Park

Cahirciveen (Co. Kerry)
t: 066 947 2806 e: **mortimer@campinginkerry.com**
alanrogers.com/IR9610 www.campinginkerry.com

Accommodation: ☑Pitch ☐ Mobile home/chalet ☐ Hotel/B&B ☐ Apartment

A tranquil, beautifully located seashore park, it is no exaggeration to describe Mannix Point as a nature lovers' paradise. Situated in one of the most spectacular parts of the Ring of Kerry, overlooking the bay and Valentia Island, the rustic seven-acre park commands splendid views in all directions. The park road meanders through the level site and offers 42 pitches of various sizes and shapes, many with shelter and seclusion. There are 42 electrical connections (10A) available. A charming, old flower bedecked fisherman's cottage has been converted to provide facilities including reception, excellent campers' kitchen and a cosy sitting room with turf fire. The knowledgeable and hospitable owner is a Bord Fáilte registered local tour guide. A keen gardener, Mortimer Moriarty laid out the site over 20 years ago and his intention to cause as little disruption to nature as possible has succeeded. The site opens directly onto marshland which teems with wildlife (a two-acre nature reserve) with direct access to the beach and seashore. A viewing platform allows observation of seals and birdlife. This is also an ideal resting place for people walking the Kerry Way.

You might like to know

You have a choice of high level or low level, long distance or short walks here. Reception are pleased to make recommendations and have plenty of maps to borrow or buy.

- ☑ Walking notes or maps available
- ☐ Waymarked footpath – direct access from site
- ☑ Waymarked footpath within 1 km. of site
- ☐ Cycle trail – direct access from site
- ☑ Cycle trail access within 2 km. of site
- ☐ Mountain bike track within 2 km. of site
- ☐ Bicycle hire on site
- ☐ Accompanied hiking trips
- ☐ Accompanied cycling trips
- ☐ Drying room for wet clothes/boots
- ☐ Packed lunch service

Facilities: Toilet and shower facilities were clean when we visited. Modern and well equipped campers' kitchen and dining area. Comfortable campers' sitting room. Laundry facilities with washing machines and dryer. Motorcaravan service point. Picnic and barbecue facilities. Fishing and boat launching from site.
Off site: Bicycle hire 800 m. Riding 3 km. Golf 14 km. Pubs, restaurants and shops 15 minutes walk. Watersports, bird watching, walking and photography. Local cruises to Skelligs Rock with free transport to and from the port for walkers and cyclists.

Open: 15 March - 15 October.

Directions: Park is 300 m. off the N70 Ring of Kerry road, 800 m. southwest of Cahirciveen (or Cahersiveen) on the road towards Waterville. GPS: 51.941517, -10.24465

Charges guide

Per unit incl. 2 persons and electricity	€ 27,00
extra person	€ 6,00

No credit cards.

Recreatiepark Klein Strand

Varsenareweg 29, B-8490 Jabbeke (West Flanders)
t: 050 811 440 e: info@kleinstrand.be
alanrogers.com/BE0555 www.kleinstrand.be

Accommodation: ☑Pitch ☑Mobile home/chalet ☐ Hotel/B&B ☐ Apartment

In a convenient location just off the A10 motorway and close to Bruges, this site is in two distinct areas divided by an access road. The touring section has 137 large pitches on flat grass separated by well trimmed hedges; all have electricity and access to water and drainage. Though surrounded by mobile homes and seasonal caravans, this is a surprisingly relaxing area and the ambience was further enhanced in 2011 when a small park was created at its centre. Some children's leisure facilities are provided here, and there is a spacious bar and a snack bar with takeaway. The main site with all the privately-owned mobile homes is closer to the lake, so has most of the amenities. These include the main reception building, restaurants, bar, minimarket, and sports facilities. This is a family holiday site and offers a comprehensive programme of activities and entertainment in July and August. The lake is used for water-skiing and has a supervised swimming area with waterslides (high season) and a beach volleyball area. Klein Strand is an ideal base from which to visit Bruges and Gent.

You might like to know
Jabbeke is located at the heart of the picturesque Brugse Ommeland, with miles of excellent walking and cycle tracks close at hand.

☑ Walking notes or maps available
☐ Waymarked footpath – direct access from site
☑ Waymarked footpath within 1 km. of site
☐ Cycle trail – direct access from site
☑ Cycle trail access within 2 km. of site
☐ Mountain bike track within 2 km. of site
☐ Bicycle hire on site
☐ Accompanied hiking trips
☐ Accompanied cycling trips
☐ Drying room for wet clothes/boots
☐ Packed lunch service

Facilities: A single modern, heated, toilet block in the touring area provides the usual facilities including good sized showers (charged) and vanity style open washbasins. Baby room. Basic facilities for disabled campers. Laundry area. Additional toilet facilities behind the touring field reception building (open July/Aug). Motorcaravan service point. Bar and snack bar. Play area. Fun pool for small children. In main park: European and Chinese restaurants, bar and snack bar, takeaways (all year). Shop (Easter-end Aug). Tennis courts and sports field. Water-ski school; water-ski shows (Sundays in July/Aug). Bicycle hire. Cable TV point (included) and WiFi (charged, first hour free) on all pitches. Off site: Riding 5 km. Beach 8 km. Golf and sailing 10 km.

Open: All year.

Directions: Jabbeke is 12 km. southwest of Bruges. From A18/A10 motorways, take exit 6/6B (Jabbeke). At roundabout take first exit signed for site. In 650 m. on left-hand bend, turn left to site in 600 m. Main reception is on left but in high season continue to touring site on right in 200 m. GPS: 51.18448, 3.10445

Charges guide

Per unit incl. up to 4 persons and electricity	€ 20,00 - € 36,00
dog	€ 2,00

Camping Floréal Kempen

Herentalsesteenweg 64, B-2460 Lichtaart (Antwerp)
t: 014 556 120 e: kempen@florealgroup.be
alanrogers.com/BE0665 www.florealgroup.be

Accommodation: ☑Pitch ☑Mobile home/chalet ☐ Hotel/B&B ☐ Apartment

This is an attractive woodland site and a member of the Floréal group. It is located close to the well known Purperen Heide, a superb nature reserve with 15 scenic footpaths leading through it. There are 207 pitches, of which only 26 are reserved for touring units. These are of a good size (100 sq.m. or more), all with 10A electricity and most with their own water supply. Several simple cabins are available for hikers, as well as fully equipped mobile homes. There are some good leisure facilities, including tennis and a multisports pitch, as well as a popular bar and restaurant. Day trips to Antwerp are very much a possibility. The old city is a gem with a great deal of interest, including over a thousand noted monuments, a diamond museum and the Rubens trail. Another popular visit is to the charming Bobbejaanlaand amusement park. There are miles of forest trails and the site's friendly managers will be pleased to recommend routes.

You might like to know

A number of hiker's cabins are available for rent on a one-night basis – ideal for those attempting some of the region's excellent long-distance footpaths.

- ☑ Walking notes or maps available
- ☐ Waymarked footpath – direct access from site
- ☑ Waymarked footpath within 1 km. of site
- ☐ Cycle trail – direct access from site
- ☑ Cycle trail access within 2 km. of site
- ☑ Mountain bike track within 2 km. of site
- ☐ Bicycle hire on site
- ☐ Accompanied hiking trips
- ☐ Accompanied cycling trips
- ☐ Drying room for wet clothes/boots
- ☐ Packed lunch service

Facilities: Toilet facilities are in need of some investment. When we visited cleaning and maintenance needed attention. Motorcaravan services. Shop. Bar. Restaurant. TV room. Tennis. Play area. Multisport terrain. Bicycle hire. Tourist information. Mobile homes for rent. WiFi throughout. Off site: Walking and cycling tracks. Golf. Antwerp. Bobbejaanlaan amusement park

Open: All year.

Directions: Approaching from Antwerp, head east on A21 motorway as far as exit 24 (Turnhout). Leave here and head south on N19 to Kasterlee, and then west on N123 to Lichtaart. Follow signs to the site. GPS: 51.21024, 4.90423

Charges guide

Per unit incl. 2 persons	€ 18,40 - € 25,70
extra person	€ 4,70
child (3-11 yrs)	€ 3,30
dog (max. 1)	€ 3,80

Camping Tonny

Tonny 35, B-6680 Amberloup (Luxembourg)
t: 061 688 285 e: camping.tonny@skynet.be
alanrogers.com/BE0720 www.campingtonny.be

Accommodation: ☑Pitch ☑Mobile home/chalet ☐ Hotel/B&B ☐ Apartment

The new Dutch owners here are rightly proud of their site. With a friendly atmosphere, it is an attractive, small campsite in a pleasant valley by the River Ourthe. A family site, there are 75 grass touring pitches, with wooden chalet buildings giving a Tirolean feel. The pitches (80-100 sq.m) are separated by small shrubs and fir trees, electricity (4/6A) is available. Cars are parked away from the units and there is a separate meadow for tents. Surrounded by natural woodland, Camping Tonny is an ideal base for outdoor activities. In bad weather, the homely bar acts as a meeting place. There is a freestanding fireplace and a shady terrace for relaxing outside. The bar is open all year (according to demand). Nearby St Hubert has a Basilica, the St Michel Furnace Industrial Museum and a wildlife park, with wild boar, deer and other native species – all worth a visit.

You might like to know

Hiking trips for teenagers are organised periodically – a great way to get to know the local flora and fauna.

- ☑ Walking notes or maps available
- ☐ Waymarked footpath – direct access from site
- ☑ Waymarked footpath within 1 km. of site
- ☐ Cycle trail – direct access from site
- ☑ Cycle trail access within 2 km. of site
- ☑ Mountain bike track within 2 km. of site
- ☑ Bicycle hire on site
- ☑ Accompanied hiking trips
- ☐ Accompanied cycling trips
- ☐ Drying room for wet clothes/boots
- ☐ Packed lunch service

Facilities: Two fully equipped sanitary units (both heated in cool weather) include showers on payment. Baby area and laundry. Freezer for campers use. Small shop. TV lounge and library. Sports field. Boules. Games room. Playgrounds. Bowling alley. Bicycle hire. Fishing. Cross-country skiing. WiFi (charged).

Open: 15 March - 15 November.

Directions: From N4 take exit for Libramont at km. 131 (N826), then to Amberloup (4 km) where site is signed just outside of the southwest town boundary. GPS: 50.02657, 5.51283

Charges guide

Per unit incl. 2 persons and electricity	€ 20,00 - € 22,00
extra person	€ 3,60 - € 4,00
child (0-12 yrs)	€ 2,25 - € 2,50

BELGIUM – Dochamps

Panoramacamping Petite Suisse

Al Bounire 27, B-6960 Dochamps (Luxembourg)
t: 084 444 030   e: info@petitesuisse.be
alanrogers.com/BE0735   www.petitesuisse.be

Accommodation: ☑Pitch ☑Mobile home/chalet ☐ Hotel/B&B ☐ Apartment

This quiet site is set in the picturesque countryside of the Belgian Ardennes, a region in which rivers flow through valleys bordered by vast forests where horses are still usefully employed. Set on a southerly slope, the site is mostly open and offers wide views of the surrounding countryside. The 193 touring pitches, all with 10A electricity, are either on open sloping ground or in terraced rows with hedges in between, and trees providing some separation. Gravel roads provide access around the site. To the right of the entrance barrier a large wooden building houses reception, a bar and a restaurant. Close by is an attractive, heated outdoor swimming pool with wide terraces surrounded by grass. Behind this is a large play area adjoining a small terrace. Although the site has many activities on offer, the opportunity should not be missed to make excursions into the countryside with its hills and forests. The villages are filled with houses built from the local stone and small inviting bars and restaurants just waiting to be visited.

You might like to know

Petite Suisse is located at the heart of the Belgian Ardennes, close to the well known villages of Durbuy and La Roche en Ardenne. There is usually plenty of snow in the winter and cross-country skiing is popular. The ski area of Baraque de Fraiture is 8 km. away.

☑ Walking notes or maps available
☐ Waymarked footpath – direct access from site
☑ Waymarked footpath within 1 km. of site
☐ Cycle trail – direct access from site
☑ Cycle trail access within 2 km. of site
☑ Mountain bike track within 2 km. of site
☐ Bicycle hire on site
☐ Accompanied hiking trips
☐ Accompanied cycling trips
☐ Drying room for wet clothes/boots
☐ Packed lunch service

Facilities: All the facilities that one would expect of a large site are available. Showers are free, washbasins both open and in cabins. Baby room. Laundry room with washing machines and dryers. Shop, restaurant, bar and takeaway (2/4-5/11). Heated outdoor swimming pool (1/5-1/9), paddling pool and slide. Sports field. Tennis. Bicycle hire. Playground and club for children. Entertainment programme during school holidays. Varied activity programme, including archery, canoeing, climbing, abseiling and walking. WiFi (charged). Off site: La Roche en Ardennes and Baraque de Fraiture (ski resort) 10 km. Golf 20 km.

Open: All year.

Directions: From E25/A26 autoroute (Liège-Luxembourg) take exit 50 then the N89 southwest towards La Roche. After 8 km. turn right (north) on N841 to Dochamps where site is signed. GPS: 50.23127, 5.62583

Charges guide

Per unit incl. 2 persons and electricity	€ 21,20 - € 42,20
extra person (over 4 yrs)	€ 4,25 - € 7,25
dog (high season max. 1)	€ 2,00 - € 5,00

Camping le Vieux Moulin

Petite Strument 62, B-6980 La Roche-en-Ardenne (Luxembourg)
t: **084 411 380**   e: info@strument.com
alanrogers.com/BE0770   www.strument.com

Accommodation: ☑Pitch ☐ Mobile home/chalet   ☐ Hotel/B&B ☐ Apartment

Located in one of the most beautiful valleys in the heart of the Ardennes, le Vieux Moulin has 183 pitches and, although there are 127 long stay units at the far end of the site, the 60 touring pitches do have their own space. Some are separated by hedges, others for tents and smaller units are more open, all are on grass, and there are 50 electric hook-ups (6A). The 19th-century watermill has been owned and operated by the owner's family for many years, but has now been converted into a small hotel and a fascinating mill museum. Visits are possible with an audio guide in English. La Roche is a pretty little town in an unspoiled area, a very scenic region of rolling tree-clad hills and small deep valleys, with rocks for climbing, castles to explore and rivers to fish.

You might like to know

Various sports are on offer here including canoeing, tennis and even parascending.

- ☑ Walking notes or maps available
- ☐ Waymarked footpath – direct access from site
- ☑ Waymarked footpath within 1 km. of site
- ☐ Cycle trail – direct access from site
- ☑ Cycle trail access within 2 km. of site
- ☐ Mountain bike track within 2 km. of site
- ☐ Bicycle hire on site
- ☐ Accompanied hiking trips
- ☐ Accompanied cycling trips
- ☐ Drying room for wet clothes/boots
- ☐ Packed lunch service

Facilities: A newly constructed, centrally located toilet block is between the touring and long stay areas. It can be heated in cool weather and provides washbasins in cubicles and controllable hot showers on payment. Washing machine. No facilities for disabled campers. A further older unit is at the end of the mill building. Restaurant and bar with hotel (8 rooms). Mill museum. Off site: Town facilities 800 m.

Open: 1 April - 11 November.

Directions: From town centre take N89 south towards St Hubert, turning right towards Hives where site is signed. Site is 800 m. from the town centre. GPS: 50.17362, 5.57750

Charges guide

Per unit incl. 2 persons	
and electricity	€ 16,00 - € 18,50
extra person	€ 2,50
dog	€ 2,00

LUXEMBOURG – Larochette

Camping Birkelt

1 Um Birkelt, L-7633 Larochette
t: 879 040   e: info@camping-birkelt.lu
alanrogers.com/LU7610   www.camping-birkelt.lu

Accommodation: ☑Pitch ☑Mobile home/chalet ☐ Hotel/B&B ☐ Apartment

This is very much a family site, with a great range of facilities provided. It is well organised and well laid out, set in an elevated position in attractive, undulating countryside. A tarmac road runs around the site with 427 large grass pitches (280 for touring), some slightly sloping, many with a fair amount of shade, on either side of gravel access roads in straight rows and circles. Two hundred pitches have electricity, 134 serviced ones have 16A, the remainder 10A. An all weather swimming pool complex is beside the site entrance (free for campers) and entertainment for children is arranged in high season. The site is very popular with tour operators (140 pitches). The main activities take place adjacent to the large circular, all-weather, family pool. This is an outdoor pool in high season and covered and heated in cooler weather. Several play areas are dotted all over the site. The entrance to the site has been made vehicle free (vehicle entrance is on a separate road) and provides a pleasant terrace and shopping area. Seven serviced, overnight motorcaravan pitches are provided in the car park area. Throughout the site, all signage is in four languages including English.

You might like to know

The Müllerthal is renowned for its splendid forests, sandstone rocks and its medieval castles in Larochette and Beaufort. The best way to enjoy it is on foot or by bicycle.

☑ Walking notes or maps available
☐ Waymarked footpath – direct access from site
☑ Waymarked footpath within 1 km. of site
☐ Cycle trail – direct access from site
☑ Cycle trail access within 2 km. of site
☐ Mountain bike track within 2 km. of site
☐ Bicycle hire on site
☐ Accompanied hiking trips
☐ Accompanied cycling trips
☐ Drying room for wet clothes/boots
☐ Packed lunch service

Facilities: Three modern heated sanitary buildings well situated around the site include mostly open washbasins (6 cabins in one block). Baby baths. Facilities (including accommodation to rent) for wheelchair users. Washing machines and dryers. Motorcaravan service point. Shops. Coffee bar. Restaurant with terrace. Outdoor swimming pool (heated 15/5-15/9). Outdoor pool for toddlers. Sauna. Play areas. Trampolines. Volleyball. Minigolf. Tennis. Bicycle hire. Riding. Balloon flights. Free WiFi over site. Off site: Golf 5 km. Fishing and kayaking 10 km.

Open: 16 March - 3 November.

Directions: From N7 (Diekirch-Luxembourg City), turn onto N8 (CR118) at Berschblach (just past Mersch) towards Larochette. Site is signed on the right 1.5 km. from Larochette. Approach road is fairly steep and narrow.
GPS: 49.78508, 6.21033

Charges guide

Per unit incl. 2 persons and electricity	€ 19,50 - € 36,00
with water and drainage	€ 22,50 - € 39,00
extra person	€ 4,25
dog	€ 2,50

Camping Kohnenhof

Kounenhaff 1, L-9838 Eisenbach
t: 929 464 e: kohnenhof@pt.lu
alanrogers.com/LU7680 www.campingkohnenhof.lu

Accommodation: ☑Pitch ☑Mobile home/chalet ☐ Hotel/B&B ☐ Apartment

Nestling in a valley with the River Our running through it, Camping Kohnenhof offers a very agreeable location for a relaxing family holiday. From the minute you stop at the reception you are assured of a warm and friendly welcome. There are 105 pitches, 80 for touring, all with 6/16A electricity. Numerous paths cross through the wooded hillside so this could be a haven for walkers. A little bridge crosses the small river over the border to Germany. The river is shallow and safe for children (parental supervision essential). A large sports field and play area with a selection of equipment caters for younger campers. During the high season, an entertainment programme is organised for parents and children. The owner organises special golf weeks with games on different courses and discounts have been agreed at several local courses (contact the site for details). The restaurant is part of an old farmhouse and offers a wonderful ambience to enjoy a meal.

You might like to know

There are several outstanding hiking trails close at hand including the GR5 which end in Nice and the classic pilgrims route (E3) to Santiago de Compostela.

☐ Walking notes or maps available
☐ Waymarked footpath – direct access from site
☑ Waymarked footpath within 1 km. of site
☐ Cycle trail – direct access from site
☑ Cycle trail access within 2 km. of site
☑ Mountain bike track within 2 km. of site
☑ Bicycle hire on site
☐ Accompanied hiking trips
☐ Accompanied cycling trips
☐ Drying room for wet clothes/boots
☐ Packed lunch service

Facilities: Heated sanitary block with showers and washbasins in cabins. Facilities for disabled visitors. Motorcaravan service point. Laundry. Bar, restaurant, takeaway (open all season). Baker calls daily. Games/TV room. Sports field with play equipment. Boules. Bicycle hire. Golf weeks. Discounts on six local 18-hole golf courses. WiFi over site. Apartments to rent. Off site: Bus to Clervaux and Vianden stops (4 times daily) outside site entrance. Riding 5 km. Castle at Vianden 14 km. Monastery at Clervaux 14 km. Golf 15 km.

Open: 30 March - 4 November.

Directions: Take N7 north from Diekirch. At Hosingen, turn right onto the narrow and winding CR324 signed Eisenbach. Follow site signs from Eisenbach or Obereisenbach.
GPS: 50.01602, 6.13600

Charges guide

Per unit incl. 2 persons and electricity	€ 19,90 - € 28,00
extra person	€ 5,00
dog	€ 3,00

Camping Fuussekaul

4 Fuussekaul, L-9156 Heiderscheid
t: 268 8881   e: info@fuussekaul.lu
alanrogers.com/LU7850   www.fuussekaul.lu

Accommodation: ☑Pitch ☑Mobile home/chalet ☐ Hotel/B&B ☑ Apartment

This site lies in the rolling wooded hills of central Luxembourg, not far from the lakes of the Sûre river dam. Of the 370 pitches, 220 of varying sizes are for touring units, all with a 6A electricity connection. There are some super pitches with private electricity and water. The site consists of winding roads, some sloping, along which the pitches are set in shaded areas. The touring area (separate from the chalets and seasonal pitches) is well endowed with modern facilities, although there is no provision for visitors with disabilities. Children who visit Fuussekaul (the name means fox hole) won't want to leave as there is so much for them to do. There is a fun pool, a paddling pool, exciting play areas, and an entertainment programme for all ages. This includes little shows and theatre productions, and various sporting activities. Adult visitors can be pampered in the spa/sauna/fitness centre and enjoy meals in a new restaurant. On the opposite side of the road (pedestrian access via an under-road passage) is Camping Reenert, a naturist site owned by the same people and permitted to use the Fuussekaul facilities. Also across the road is a service and parking area for six motorcaravans.

You might like to know
This is a heavily wooded area with some excellent trails leading through the forest to pretty rural villages.

- ☑ Walking notes or maps available
- ☐ Waymarked footpath – direct access from site
- ☑ Waymarked footpath within 1 km. of site
- ☐ Cycle trail – direct access from site
- ☑ Cycle trail access within 2 km. of site
- ☐ Mountain bike track within 2 km. of site
- ☐ Bicycle hire on site
- ☐ Accompanied hiking trips
- ☐ Accompanied cycling trips
- ☐ Drying room for wet clothes/boots
- ☐ Packed lunch service

Facilities: Four excellent sanitary blocks provide showers (token € 0.75), washbasins (in cabins and communal) and children and baby rooms with small toilets, washbasins and showers. Laundry. Parking and service area for motorcaravans. Well stocked shop. Bar. Restaurant and takeaway. Swimming pools. Suite with sauna and sun beds. Beauty salon. Playgrounds. Cross-country skiing when snow permits. Bicycle hire. Children's club. Bowling centre. WiFi (charged). Off site: Castles, museums and walks all within a reasonable distance. Bus stops outside site entrance. Riding 500 m. Fishing 3 km. Supermarket and shops in Ettelbruckt 7 km.

Open: All year.

Directions: Take N15 from Diekirch to Heiderscheid. Site is on left at top of hill just before reaching the village. Motorcaravan service area is signed on the right.
GPS: 49.87750, 5.99283

Charges guide

Per unit incl. 2 persons and electricity	€ 18,50 - € 38,00
extra person	€ 3,00
child	€ 1,00 - € 2,00
dog	€ 2,00

Camping Waalstrand

Waaldijk 23A, NL-6691 MB Gendt (Gelderland)
t: 0481 421 604 e: info@waalstrand.nl
alanrogers.com/NL5823 www.waalstrand.nl

Accommodation: ☑Pitch ☐ Mobile home/chalet ☐ Hotel/B&B ☐ Apartment

Camping Waalstrand lies just outside the village of Gendt. It is stretched out along the banks of the River Waal and backed by a dyke separating the river from the town. Many of the pitches have good views of the various boats plying the river. Surrounding the campsite is an excellent nature reserve, the Gelderese Poort, an extensive delta of river dunes, lowland forests and meadows with many walks and cycle routes. This is a quiet campsite with no organised entertainment. There are 150 average size, level, unshaded, grassy/sandy pitches with 90 for touring. All pitches have 6A electricity and a TV hook-up. Access is good for large outfits. The campsite has a pleasant snack bar and a terrace overlooking the river. The swimming pool and beach area make it an excellent site for children, and within a short distance are the well known ancient cities of Arnhem and Nijmegen with their interesting old quarters and historical connections to World War Two. Gendt, the local town, has a supermarket and various shops and restaurants.

You might like to know

Camping Waalstrand lies in the Gelderese Poort National Park with its beautiful views over the River Waal. It is ideal for walking and cycling, and an extensive network of routes start from the site (www.lekkerfietsen.nl). Visitors staying in June will receive a complimentary map.

☑ Walking notes or maps available
☐ Waymarked footpath – direct access from site
☐ Waymarked footpath within 1 km. of site
☑ Cycle trail – direct access from site
☐ Cycle trail access within 2 km. of site
☐ Mountain bike track within 2 km. of site
☑ Bicycle hire on site
☐ Accompanied hiking trips
☐ Accompanied cycling trips
☐ Drying room for wet clothes/boots
☐ Packed lunch service

Facilities: Modern clean toilet block with all necessary facilities. Washing machine/dryer. Outdoor swimming pool. Café. Terrace. Play area. Boules. Large chess set. Small sandy river beach and boat ramp. Bike hire. Motorcaravan services. Fishing. WiFi (charged). Dogs are welcome in a small area of the site and limited to one dog per pitch. Off site: Gelderse Poort National Park. Arnhem, many ancient buildings, shops, bars, cafés, zoo. World War II museum. Nijmegen, the Netherlands' oldest city. Many marked walks and cycle tracks. Boating on river. River ferries.

Open: 30 May - 1 October.

Directions: Leave A15 motorway at Bemmel between Nijmegen and Arnhem, signed Gendt (7 km). Site is signed from Gendt.
GPS: 51.87597, 5.98897

Charges guide

Per unit incl. 2 persons and electricity	€ 25,40
extra person	€ 5,00
dog	€ 3,50

No credit cards.

NETHERLANDS – Emst-Gortel

Camping De Wildhoeve

Hanendorperweg 102, NL-8166 JJ Emst-Gortel (Gelderland)
t: 0578 661 324 e: info@wildhoeve.nl
alanrogers.com/NL6285 www.wildhoeve.nl

Accommodation: ☑Pitch ☑Mobile home/chalet ☐ Hotel/B&B ☐ Apartment

Camping De Wildhoeve is an exceptional, welcoming, privately owned site with many amenities of the type one would normally find on larger holiday camps. The well maintained site is located in woodland and has 400 pitches with 330 for tourers. Pitching is in several areas, mostly in the shade of mature conifers. Partly separated by trees and bushes, the level pitches are numbered and all have 6/10A electricity, water and drainage. Behind reception is an octagonal-shaped, indoor sub-tropical pool with a large water slide and fun paddling pool. Next to reception is a water adventure playground with a small beach. To the front of the site are tennis courts and next to that is another open-air pool with a large slide. Here also is a shop plus a grand café/restaurant with terrace. Many activities are organised for children, including open-air theatre. The toilet facilities on this site are excellent and include one block that has a special children's section with an area for children with disabilities.

You might like to know
The Veluwe is a vast expanse at the heart of The Netherlands, with many miles of walking and cycle tracks.

☑ Walking notes or maps available
☐ Waymarked footpath – direct access from site
☑ Waymarked footpath within 1 km. of site
☐ Cycle trail – direct access from site
☑ Cycle trail access within 2 km. of site
☐ Mountain bike track within 2 km. of site
☐ Bicycle hire on site
☐ Accompanied hiking trips
☐ Accompanied cycling trips
☐ Drying room for wet clothes/boots
☐ Packed lunch service

Facilities: Four well placed, heated blocks with toilets, washbasins (open style and in cabins) and free, preset hot showers. Special children's section with showers, basins and toilets. Baby room. Family shower room. Facilities for disabled children. Laundry facilities. Shop, grand café/restaurant. Snack bar. Indoor and outdoor pools with slides and paddling pool. Water adventure playground. Bicycle hire. Tennis. Open-air theatre. WiFi over site (charged). Dogs are not accepted. Off site: Fishing 4 km. Riding 5 km. Paleis Het Loo. Apeldoorn. Wild Animal Park, Wissel.

Open: April - September.

Directions: From the A28, take exit 15 (Epe/Nunspeet). Continue east towards Epe and at traffic lights turn south towards Emst. Continue straight ahead at roundabout in Emst. Turn right at church, into Hanendorperweg. Site is on the right after 3.5 km. GPS: 52.31369, 5.92707

Charges guide

Per unit incl. 2 persons and electricity	€ 21,00 - € 37,75
extra person	€ 5,00

Molecaten Park De Koerberg

Koerbergseweg 4/1, NL-8181 LL Heerde (Gelderland)

t: **0578 699 810** e: **dekoerberg@molecaten.nl**

alanrogers.com/NL6355 www.molecaten.nl/dekoerberg

Accommodation: ☑Pitch ☑Mobile home/chalet ☐ Hotel/B&B ☐ Apartment

Molecaten Park De Koerberg is located in the extensive Veluwe region. This is a spacious site with 132 large, well shaded touring pitches set on sheltered fields in the woods. Special hiker's pitches and simple cabins are available. Accommodation to rent includes a fully equipped De Waard tent and bungalows for 4-6 persons. The new reception and site restaurant are welcoming and form the centre of the complex. The restaurant offers a tempting range of local dishes (including takeaway meals). Breakfast can be delivered to your pitch if you wish. A bowling centre is also available and is great fun for a night out with a difference. A lively programme of activities and entertainment is arranged in high season. A club for children is held with many activities organised by the site's mascots, Molly and Caatje. Off site, there is plenty to do including a chocolate workshop and a bakery museum. The Kröller-Müller Van Gogh museum at Otterlo houses the world's second largest collection of the artist's work – highly recommended.

Facilities: One large, heated sanitary block in the touring area has facilities for babies and families. Shop. Bar, restaurant and takeaway food. Heated, outdoor swimming pool. Play area. Tennis. Football. Bowling alley. WiFi throughout (charged). Entertainment and activity programme. Tents and bungalows to rent. Off site: Beach, golf and riding 3 km. Fishing and boat launching 5 km. Cycle and walking tracks. Kröller-Müller museum.

Open: 1 April - 1 November.

Directions: Heading south from Zwolle, leave A50 motorway at exit 28 and follow signs to Heerde. Then follow signs to the site. GPS: 52.40965, 6.051149

Charges guide

Per unit incl. 2 persons and electricity	€ 19,25 - € 25,25
extra person	€ 3,90
child (2-10 yrs)	€ 2,90
dog (max. 1)	€ 3,90

You might like to know

The area surrounding Park Molecaten Koerberg is ideal for a wide range of outdoor activities such as walking and cycling. The adjacent Zwolle forest, the Renderklippen moraine and the Veluwe are particular attractions.

- ☑ Walking notes or maps available
- ☑ Waymarked footpath – direct access from site
- ☑ Waymarked footpath within 1 km. of site
- ☑ Cycle trail – direct access from site
- ☑ Cycle trail access within 2 km. of site
- ☑ Mountain bike track within 2 km. of site
- ☑ Bicycle hire on site
- ☑ Accompanied hiking trips
- ☐ Accompanied cycling trips
- ☐ Drying room for wet clothes/boots
- ☐ Packed lunch service

Landgoed Molecaten

Koeweg 1, NL-8051 PM Hattem (Gelderland)
t: 0384 447 044   e: landgoedmolecaten@molecaten.nl
alanrogers.com/NL6357   www.molecaten.nl/landgoedmolecaten

Accommodation: ☑Pitch ☐ Mobile home/chalet ☐ Hotel/B&B ☐ Apartment

Landgoed Molecaten can be found amongst old beech and oak trees on the southern side of the fortified town of Hattem. This is a tranquil site with large pitches, surrounded by a variety of mature trees which provide plenty of privacy and shade, perfect for those seeking peace and quiet. There are 130 hectares of woodland, flora and fauna here. Children can safely explore the woods – ideal for hide and seek. A pair of owls have been resident here for many years and are often seen at twilight. Rentable accommodation is a Boshuus, a specially designed chalet for four people, perfect for walkers and cyclists. Narrow access makes this site unsuitable for large units. An indoor and outdoor swimming pool can be found within easy walking distance. A number of theme parks are also close at hand, notably Walibi Holland, Julianatoren and Ecodrome. The Harderwijk dolphinarium is also excellent. There are more than 1,600 km. of cycle and walking tracks (some guided tours are available). For golfers there is a 9-hole golf centre and a pitch and putt course nearby.

You might like to know

Discover the beautiful Veluwe IJsselvallei area surrounding the campsite, by bicycle or on foot, or choose one of the many excursions available.

- ☑ Walking notes or maps available
- ☑ Waymarked footpath – direct access from site
- ☑ Waymarked footpath within 1 km. of site
- ☑ Cycle trail – direct access from site
- ☑ Cycle trail access within 2 km. of site
- ☑ Mountain bike track within 2 km. of site
- ☑ Bicycle hire on site
- ☑ Accompanied hiking trips
- ☐ Accompanied cycling trips
- ☐ Drying room for wet clothes/boots
- ☐ Packed lunch service

Facilities: Two centrally located, Portacabin style toilet blocks are centrally located. Some washbasins in cabins, large family shower room (hot water on payment key). Toilet facility only for disabled visitors (key access). Washing machine and dryer. Snack bar/takeaway with terrace. Play areas. Volleyball. Bicycle hire. GPS tours. Activity and entertainment programme (under 12s; high season). WiFi over site (charged). Off site: Cycling and walking tracks. Walibi Holland. Harderwijk and dolphinarium. Riding 1 km. Golf 15 km.

Open: 29 March - 30 September.

Directions: From the A50 motorway take exit 30 and follow signs towards Apeldoorn (Hattem/Hessenweg). Then follow directions to Hattem. Upon arrival here, continue ahead on to Hessenweg. Site is signed from here. GPS: 52.466955, 6.058115

Charges guide

Per unit incl. 2 persons and electricity	€ 16,00 - € 18,00
extra person	€ 2,90
child (2-10 yrs)	€ 1,90
dog (max. 1)	€ 1,90

Camping De Papillon

Kanaalweg 30, NL-7591 NH Denekamp (Overijssel)
t: 0541 351 670 e: info@depapillon.nl
alanrogers.com/NL6470 www.depapillon.nl

Accommodation: ☑Pitch ☑Mobile home/chalet ☐Hotel/B&B ☐Apartment

De Papillon is perhaps one of the best and most enjoyable campsites in the Netherlands. All 245 touring pitches are spacious (120-160 sq.m), all have electricity (4/10/16A), and 220 have water and drainage. An impressive, new sanitary block has state-of-the-art equipment and uses green technology. There is a new entertainment centre with outdoor auditorium for children, and the water play area by the adventure playground and covered, heated pool is among the most imaginative and exciting we have seen. The restored heathland area offers opportunities for nature lovers; there is also a large fishing lake and a swimming lake with beach area and activities. This friendly, welcoming site is well thought through with an eye for detail and an appreciation of nature and the environment. Waste water from the showers is used to flush the toilets, all buildings are heated by solar energy, and all waste is separated for recycling. This is a great destination for a holiday amongst nature and the green countryside of the Twente region. A trip into Germany is quick and easy.

You might like to know

There is a wonderful network of cycle tracks through Twente. Good maps are available at reception.

- ☑ Walking notes or maps available
- ☐ Waymarked footpath – direct access from site
- ☐ Waymarked footpath within 1 km. of site
- ☐ Cycle trail – direct access from site
- ☑ Cycle trail access within 2 km. of site
- ☐ Mountain bike track within 2 km. of site
- ☑ Bicycle hire on site
- ☐ Accompanied hiking trips
- ☐ Accompanied cycling trips
- ☐ Drying room for wet clothes/boots
- ☐ Packed lunch service

Facilities: Two large sanitary buildings with showers, toilets, washbasins in cabins, facilities for babies and for disabled visitors. This building is designed in the shape of a butterfly, the other was new for 2012. Laundry room. Spacious reception area with supermarket, restaurant, bar and takeaway. Heated pool with children's pool and sliding roof. Lake swimming with sandy beach. New modern adventure play area and smaller play areas. Pétanque. Bicycle hire. Fishing pond. Tennis. Pets to stroke. Max. 1 dog. Luxury bungalows to rent (good views). New water spray park for children up to 13 yrs. Free WiFi over site. Off site: Riding 12 km. Golf 15 km.

Open: 1 April - 1 October.

Directions: From the A1 take exit 32 (Oldenzaal-Denekamp) and continue to Denekamp. Pass Denekamp and turn right at village of Noord-Deurningen and follow signs to site. GPS: 52.39200, 7.04900

Charges guide

Per unit incl. 2 persons and 4A electricity	€ 27,00
incl. full services	€ 30,25
extra person	€ 4,25

Vikær Diernæs Strand Camping

Dundelum 29, Diernæs, DK-6100 Haderslev (Sønderjylland)
t: 74 57 54 64   e: info@vikaercamp.dk
alanrogers.com/DK2022   www.vikaercamp.dk

Accommodation: ☑Pitch ☑Mobile home/chalet   ☐ Hotel/B&B ☐ Apartment

Vikær Diernæs Strand Camping in Southern Jutland lies in beautiful surroundings, right on the Diernæs Bugt beaches – ideal for both active campers and relaxation seekers. There are 390 grass pitches (210 for touring units), all with 10/16A electricity and separated by low hedges. Access is from long, gravel lanes. Forty newly developed, fully serviced pitches have electricity, water, drainage, TV aerial point and Internet. From these, and from the front pitches on the lower fields, there are marvellous views over the Diernæs Bugt. A Blue Flag beach runs along one edge of the site, and it can be narrow in places. It is well used for beach games, paddling and swimming. For the active there are several routes for walking and cycling and, of course, sea fishing trips are possible. In the area are a newly developed swamp nature reserve, Schackenborg Castle and the battlefields of Dybbøl Banke.

You might like to know

Why not join in the Midsummer celebrations here – with live entertainment until midnight and a spectacular bonfire.

☑ **Walking notes or maps available**
☐ **Waymarked footpath – direct access from site**
☑ **Waymarked footpath within 1 km. of site**
☐ **Cycle trail – direct access from site**
☑ **Cycle trail access within 2 km. of site**
☐ **Mountain bike track within 2 km. of site**
☐ **Bicycle hire on site**
☐ **Accompanied hiking trips**
☐ **Accompanied cycling trips**
☐ **Drying room for wet clothes/boots**
☐ **Packed lunch service**

Facilities: Three modern toilet blocks with washbasins in cabins and controllable hot showers. Family shower rooms. Children's section. Baby room. En-suite facilities for disabled visitors. Laundry. Campers' kitchen. Motorcaravan services. Shop (July/Aug, then weekends only). Playground. Minigolf. Fishing. Archery. Watersports and boat launching. Pétanque. TV room. Play house with Lego and Play Station. Daily activities for children in high season. WiFi (charged). Torch useful. English is spoken. Off site: Golf 8 km. Bicycle hire 15 km.

Open: Week before Easter - 30 October.

Directions: From German/Danish border follow E45 north. Take exit 69 and follow to Hoptrup. From Hoptrup follow to Diernæs and Diernæs Strand. GPS: 55.15029, 9.4969

Charges guide

Per person	DKK 71
child (under 12 yrs)	DKK 47
pitch	DKK 41 - 72
electricity	DKK 35
dog	DKK 10

Fornæs Camping

Stensmarkvej 36, DK-8500 Grenå (Århus)
t: **86 33 23 30** e: **fornaes@1031.inord.dk**
alanrogers.com/DK2070 www.fornaesfamiliecamping.dk

Accommodation: ☑Pitch ☑Mobile home/chalet ☐ Hotel/B&B ☐ Apartment

In the grounds of a former farm, Fornæs Camping is about 5 km. from Grenå. From reception, a wide gravel access road descends through a large grassy field to the sea. Pitches to the left are mostly level, to the right slightly sloping with some terracing and views of the Kattegat. The rows of pitches are divided into separate areas by colourful bushes and each row is marked by a concrete tub containing a young tree and colourful flowers. Fornæs has 320 pitches of which 240 are for tourers, the others being used for seasonal visitors. All touring pitches have 10A electricity. At the foot of the site is a pebble beach with a large grass area behind it. There is also an attractive outdoor pool near the entrance with two slides, a paddling pool, sauna, solarium and whirlpool. Here a comprehensive room serves as a restaurant, takeaway and bar, and in a former barn there is a new games room. Fornæs provides a good base from which to explore this part of Denmark or for taking the ferry to Hjelm island or to Sweden.

You might like to know

Den Gamle By ('The Old Town') was founded in 1909 and was the world's first open-air museum of urban history and culture. Seventy-five historic houses from all over Denmark shape the contours of a Danish town as it might have looked in the days of Hans Christian Anderson.

☑ Walking notes or maps available
☐ Waymarked footpath – direct access from site
☑ Waymarked footpath within 1 km. of site
☐ Cycle trail – direct access from site
☑ Cycle trail access within 2 km. of site
☐ Mountain bike track within 2 km. of site
☐ Bicycle hire on site
☐ Accompanied hiking trips
☐ Accompanied cycling trips
☐ Drying room for wet clothes/boots
☐ Packed lunch service

Facilities: Two partly refurbished toilet blocks have British style toilets, washbasins in cabins and controllable hot showers. Children's section and baby room. Family shower rooms. Facilities for disabled visitors. Fully equipped laundry. Campers' kitchen. Motorcaravan service point. Shop. Café/grill with bar and takeaway (evenings). Swimming pool (80 sq.m) with paddling pool. Sauna and solarium. Play area and adventure playground. Games room with satellite TV. Minigolf. Fishing. Watersports. Off site: Golf and riding 5 km.

Open: 15 March - 20 September.

Directions: From Århus follow the 15 road towards Grenå and then the 16 road towards town centre. Turn north and follow signs for Fornæs and the site. GPS: 56.45602, 10.94107

Charges guide

Per person	DKK 85
child (1-12 yrs)	DKK 45
electricity (10A)	DKK 35
dog	DKK 15

Credit cards 5% surcharge.

Klim Strand Camping

Havvejen 167, Klim Strand, DK-9690 Fjerritslev (Nordjylland)
t: **98 22 53 40**   e: **ksc@klim-strand.dk**
alanrogers.com/DK2170   www.klim-strand.dk

Accommodation: ☑Pitch ☑Mobile home/chalet   ☐ Hotel/B&B   ☐ Apartment

A large family holiday site right beside the sea, Klim Strand is a paradise for children. It is a privately owned TopCamp site with a full complement of quality facilities, including its own fire engine and trained staff. The site has 460 numbered touring pitches, all with electricity (10A), laid out in rows, many divided by trees and hedges, with shade in parts. Some 220 of these are extra large (180 sq.m) and fully serviced with electricity, water, drainage and TV hook-up. On-site activities include an outdoor water slide complex, an indoor pool, tennis courts and pony riding (all free). A wellness spa centre including a pirate-themed indoor play hall is a recent addition. For children there are numerous play areas, an adventure playground with aerial cable ride and a roller skating area. There is a kayak school and a large bouncy castle for toddlers. Live music and dancing are organised twice a week in high season. Suggested excursions include trips to offshore islands, visits to local potteries, a brewery museum and birdwatching on the Bygholm Vejle. A member of Leading Campings group.

You might like to know
After a day's walking or cycling you can enjoy being pampered at the site's first rate wellness and spa centre.

☑ Walking notes or maps available
☐ Waymarked footpath – direct access from site
☑ Waymarked footpath within 1 km. of site
☐ Cycle trail – direct access from site
☑ Cycle trail access within 2 km. of site
☐ Mountain bike track within 2 km. of site
☐ Bicycle hire on site
☐ Accompanied hiking trips
☐ Accompanied cycling trips
☐ Drying room for wet clothes/boots
☐ Packed lunch service

Facilities: Two good, large, heated toilet blocks are central, with spacious showers and some washbasins in cubicles. Separate children's room. Baby rooms. Bathrooms for families (some charged) and disabled visitors. Laundry. Well equipped kitchens and barbecue areas. TV lounges. Motorcaravan services. Pizzeria. Supermarket, restaurant and bar (all season). Pool complex. Wellness centre with sauna, solariums, whirlpool bath, fitness room and indoor play hall. TV rental. Play areas. Crèche. Bicycle hire. Cabins to rent. WiFi over part of site (charged). Off site: Golf 10 km. Boat launching 25 km.

Open: 30 March - 21 October.

Directions: Turn off Thisted-Fjerritslev 11 road to Klim from where site is signed.
GPS: 57.133333, 9.166667

Charges guide

Per unit incl. 2 persons and electricity	€ 31,00 - € 50,30
extra person	€ 11,00
child (1-11 yrs)	€ 8,20

Lærdal Ferie & Fritidspark

Grandavegens, N-6886 Lærdal (Sogn og Fjordane)

t: **57 66 66 95** e: **info@laerdalferiepark.com**

alanrogers.com/NO2375 www.laerdalferiepark.com

Accommodation: ☑ Pitch ☑ Mobile home/chalet ☑ Hotel/B&B ☑ Apartment

This site is beside the famous Sognefjord, the longest fjord in the world. It is ideally situated if you want to explore the glaciers, fjords and waterfalls of the region. The 100 pitches are level with well trimmed grass, connected by tarmac roads and are suitable for tents, caravans and motorcaravans. There are 80 electrical hook-ups. The fully licensed restaurant serves traditional meals as well as snacks and pizzas. The pretty little village of Laerdal, only 400 m. away, is well worth a visit. A walk among the old, small wooden houses is a pleasant and interesting experience. You can hire boats on the site for short trips on the fjord. Guided hiking, cycling and fishing trips are also available. The site also provides cabins, flats and rooms to rent, plus a brand new motel, all very modern and extremely tastefully designed.

You might like to know

There are some great hikes in the area – enjoy a fantastic accompanied walk from the fjord to the mountain summit with stunning views of Lærdal.

- ☑ Walking notes or maps available
- ☐ Waymarked footpath – direct access from site
- ☑ Waymarked footpath within 1 km. of site
- ☐ Cycle trail – direct access from site
- ☑ Cycle trail access within 2 km. of site
- ☑ Mountain bike track within 2 km. of site
- ☑ Bicycle hire on site
- ☑ Accompanied hiking trips
- ☑ Accompanied cycling trips
- ☐ Drying room for wet clothes/boots
- ☐ Packed lunch service

Facilities: Two modern and well decorated sanitary blocks with washbasins (some in cubicles), showers on payment, and toilets. Facilities for disabled visitors. Children's room. Washing machine and dryer. Kitchen. Motorcaravan services. Small shop. Bar, restaurant and takeaway (20/5-5/9). TV room. Playground. Motorboats, rowing boats, canoes, bicycles and pedal cars for hire. Bicycle hire. Fishing. WiFi at reception. Off site: Cruises on the Sognefjord 400 m. The Norwegian Wild Salmon Centre 400 m. Riding 500 m. Golf 12 km. The Flåm railway 40 km.

Open: All year (by telephone request 1 Nov-14 March).

Directions: Site is on road 5 (from the Oslo-Bergen road, E16) 400 m. north of Laerdal village centre. GPS: 61.10037, 7.46986

Charges guide

Per unit incl. 2 persons and electricity	NOK 210
extra person	NOK 50
child (4-15 yrs)	NOK 25

NORWAY – Sogndal

Kjørnes Camping

N-6856 Sogndal (Sogn og Fjordane)
t: 57 67 45 80 e: camping@kjornes.no
alanrogers.com/NO2390 www.kjornes.no

Accommodation: ☑Pitch ☑Mobile home/chalet ☐ Hotel/B&B ☑ Apartment

Kjørnes Camping is idyllically situated on the Sognefjord, three kilometres from the centre of Sogndal. It occupies a long open meadow which is terraced down to the waterside. The site has 100 pitches for camping units (all with electricity), 14 cabins and two apartments for rent. Located at the very centre of the 'fjord kingdom' by the main no. 5 road, this site is the ideal base from which to explore the Sognefjord. You are within a short drive (maximum one hour) from all the major attractions including the Jostedal glacier, the Nærøyfjord, the Flåm Railway, the Urnes Stave Church and Sognefjellet. This site is ideal for those who enjoy peace and quiet, lovely scenery or a spot of fishing. Access is via a narrow lane with passing places, which drops down towards the fjord three kilometres from Sogndal.

You might like to know
Why not try a glacier walk combined with kayaking on the glacier lake. Accompanied trips are available with or without overnight accommodation.

- ☑ Walking notes or maps available
- ☐ Waymarked footpath – direct access from site
- ☑ Waymarked footpath within 1 km. of site
- ☐ Cycle trail – direct access from site
- ☑ Cycle trail access within 2 km. of site
- ☑ Mountain bike track within 2 km. of site
- ☐ Bicycle hire on site
- ☑ Accompanied hiking trips
- ☐ Accompanied cycling trips
- ☐ Drying room for wet clothes/boots
- ☐ Packed lunch service

Facilities: A high quality sanitary building was added in 2008. Baby room. Facilities for disabled visitors. A new building provides a kitchen with cooking facilities, dishwasher, a dining area overlooking the fjord, and laundry facilities. Small shop (20/6-20/8). Satellite TV, WiFi throughout (free). Off site: Hiking, glacier walks, climbing, rafting, walking around Sognefjord. Details from reception. Bicycle hire 3 km.

Open: 1 May - 1 October.

Directions: Site is off the Rv 5, 3 km. east of Sogndal, 8 km. west of Kaupanger.
GPS: 61.21164, 7.12108

Charges guide

Per unit incl. 2 persons and electricity	NOK 270
extra person	NOK 15
child (4-16 yrs)	NOK 10

Trollveggen Camping

Horgheimseidet, N-6300 Åndalsnes (Møre og Romsdal)
t: 71 22 37 00 e: post@trollveggen.no
alanrogers.com/NO2452 www.trollveggen.no

Accommodation: ☑Pitch ☑Mobile home/chalet ☐Hotel/B&B ☑Apartment

The location of this site provides a unique experience – it is set at the foot of the famous vertical cliff of Trollveggen (the Troll Wall), which is Europe's highest vertical mountain face. The site is pleasantly laid out in terraces with level grass pitches. The facility block, four cabins and reception are all very attractively built with grass roofs. Beside the river is an attractive barbecue area where barbecue parties are sometimes arranged. This site is a must for people who love nature. The site is surrounded by the Troll Peaks and the Romsdalshorn Mountains with the rapid river of Rauma flowing by. Here in the beautiful valley of Romsdalen you have the ideal starting point for trips to many outstanding attractions such as 'The Troll Road' to Geiranger or to the Mardalsfossen waterfalls. In the mountains there are nature trails of various lengths and difficulties. The campsite owners are happy to help you with information. The town of Åndalsnes is 10 km. away and has a long tourism tradition as a place to visit. It is situated in the inner part of the beautiful Romsdalfjord and has a range of shops and restaurants.

You might like to know
The Romsdal Alps area offers numerous hiking trails, many close to Trollveggen Camping. Romsdalseggen, in particular, is a very popular hike, with wonderful views of the surrounding mountains and the Romsdal valley. From Trollveggen Camping you can cycle along the idyllic, local roads all the way to Åndalsnes town, 10 km. away.

- ☑ Walking notes or maps available
- ☑ Waymarked footpath – direct access from site
- ☐ Waymarked footpath within 1 km. of site
- ☑ Cycle trail – direct access from site
- ☐ Cycle trail access within 2 km. of site
- ☐ Mountain bike track within 2 km. of site
- ☑ Bicycle hire on site
- ☑ Accompanied hiking trips
- ☐ Accompanied cycling trips
- ☑ Drying room for wet clothes/boots
- ☐ Packed lunch service

Facilities: One heated toilet block provides washbasins, some in cubicles, and showers on payment. Family room with baby bath and changing mat, plus facilities for disabled visitors. Communal kitchen with cooking rings, small ovens, fridge and sinks (free hot water). Laundry facilities. Motorcaravan service point. Barbecue area (covered). Playground. Duck pond. WiFi throughout (free). Off site: Climbing, glacier walking and hiking. Fjord fishing. Sightseeing trips. The Troll Road. Mardalsfossen (waterfall). Geiranger and Åndalsnes.

Open: 10 May - 20 September.

Directions: Site is located on the E136 road, 10 km. south of Åndalsnes. It is signed. GPS: 62.49444, 7.758333

Charges guide

Per unit incl. 2 persons and electricity	NOK 229
extra person (over 4 yrs)	NOK 12

Neset Camping

N-4741 Byglandsfjord (Aust-Agder)
t: 37 93 42 55 e: post@neset.no
alanrogers.com/NO2610 www.neset.no

Accommodation: ☑Pitch ☑Mobile home/chalet ☐ Hotel/B&B ☐ Apartment

On a semi-promontory on the shores of the 40 km. long Byglandsfjord, Neset is a good centre for activities or as a stop en route north from the ferry port of Kristiansand (from England or Denmark). Neset is situated on well kept grassy meadows by the lake shore, with water on three sides and the road on the fourth, and provides 200 unmarked pitches with electricity and cable TV available. The main building houses reception, a small shop and a restaurant with fine views over the water. This is a well run, friendly site where one could spend an active few days. Byglandsfjord offers good fishing (mainly trout) and the area has marked trails for cycling, riding or walking in an area famous for its minerals.

You might like to know

There are some great walks leading from the campsite, overlooking the picturesque Lake Byglangsfjorden.

☑ Walking notes or maps available
☐ Waymarked footpath – direct access from site
☑ Waymarked footpath within 1 km. of site
☐ Cycle trail – direct access from site
☑ Cycle trail access within 2 km. of site
☐ Mountain bike track within 2 km. of site
☐ Bicycle hire on site
☐ Accompanied hiking trips
☐ Accompanied cycling trips
☐ Drying room for wet clothes/boots
☐ Packed lunch service

Facilities: Three modern sanitary blocks which can be heated, all with comfortable hot showers (some on payment), washing up facilities (metered hot water) and a kitchen. Restaurant and takeaway (15/6-15/8). Shop (1/5-1/10). Campers' kitchen. Playground. Lake swimming, boating and fishing. Excellent new barbecue area and hot tub. Bicycle, canoe and pedalo hire. Climbing, rafting and canoeing courses arranged (including trips to see beavers and elk). Cross-country skiing possible in winter. Off site: Rock climbing wall. Marked forest trails.

Open: All year.

Directions: Site is on route 9, 2.5 km. north of the town of Byglandsfjord on the eastern shores of the lake. GPS: 58.68848, 7.80132

Charges guide

Per unit incl. 2 persons and electricity	NOK 30

Röstånga Camping & Bad

Blinkarpsvägen 3, S-268 68 Röstånga (Skåne Län)
t: 043 591 064 e: nystrand@msn.com
alanrogers.com/SW2630 www.rostangacamping.se

Accommodation: ☑Pitch ☑Mobile home/chalet ☐ Hotel/B&B ☐ Apartment

Beside the Söderåsen National Park, this scenic campsite has its own fishing lake and many activities for the whole family. There are 180 large, level, grassy pitches with electricity (10A) and a quiet area for tents with a view over the fishing lake. The tent area has its own service building and several barbecue places. A large holiday home and 21 pleasant cabins are available to rent all year round. A pool complex adjacent to the site provides a 50 m. swimming pool, three children's pools and a water slide, all heated during peak season. Activities are arranged on the site in high season, including a children's club with exciting activities such as treasure hunts and gold panning, and for adults, aquarobics, Nordic walking and tennis. The Söderåsen National Park offers hiking and bicycle trails. The friendly staff will be happy to help you to plan interesting excursions in the area.

You might like to know

Why not try some Nordic walking?
Equipment can be borrowed from reception.

☑ Walking notes or maps available
☐ Waymarked footpath – direct access from site
☑ Waymarked footpath within 1 km. of site
☐ Cycle trail – direct access from site
☑ Cycle trail access within 2 km. of site
☐ Mountain bike track within 2 km. of site
☐ Bicycle hire on site
☐ Accompanied hiking trips
☐ Accompanied cycling trips
☐ Drying room for wet clothes/boots
☐ Packed lunch service

Facilities: Four good, heated sanitary blocks with free hot water and facilities for babies and disabled visitors. Motorcaravan service point. Laundry with washing machines and dryers. Kitchen with cooking rings, oven and microwave. Small shop at reception. Bar, restaurant and takeaway. Minigolf. Tennis. Fitness trail. Fishing. Canoe hire. Children's club. WiFi (free). Off site: Swimming pool complex adjacent to site (free for campers as is a visit to the zoo). Golf 11 km. Motor racing track at Ring Knutstorp 8 km.

Open: 10 April - 30 September.

Directions: From Malmö: drive towards Lund and follow road no. 108 to Röstånga. From Stockholm: turn off at Östra Ljungby and take road no. 13 to Röstånga. In Röstånga drive through the village on road no. 108 and follow the signs. GPS: 55.996583, 13.28005

Charges guide

Per unit incl. 2 persons
and electricity   € 25,00 - € 33,00

SWEDEN – Färjestaden

Krono Camping Saxnäs

S-386 95 Färjestaden (Kalmar Län)
t: 048 535 700   e: info@kcsaxnas.se
alanrogers.com/SW2680   www.kcsaxnas.se

Accommodation: ☑Pitch ☑Mobile home/chalet ☐ Hotel/B&B ☐ Apartment

Well placed for touring Sweden's Riviera and the fascinating and beautiful island of
Öland, this family run site, part of the Krono group, has 420 marked and numbered
touring pitches. Arranged in rows on open, well kept grassland dotted with a few trees,
all have electricity (10/16A), 320 have TV connections and 112 also have water. An
unmarked area without electricity can accommodate around 60 tents. The site has about
130 long stay units and cabins for rent. The sandy beach slopes very gently and is safe
for children. Reception is efficient and friendly with good English spoken. In 2009 an
outdoor heated pool and a children's pool were built at the entrance to the site.
In high season children's games are organised and dances are held twice weekly, with
other activities on other evenings. Nearby attractions include the 7 km. long Öland road
bridge and the 400 old windmills on the island (in the 19th century there were 2,000).
The southern tip of Öland, Ottenby, is a paradise for birdwatchers.

You might like to know

Öland is known as the island of the sun and
wind and is an enchanting area, known far
beyond the borders of Sweden. There are
some great walks on the island; alternatively
the mainland is easily accessed by a bridge.

☑ Walking notes or maps available
☐ Waymarked footpath – direct access from site
☐ Waymarked footpath within 1 km. of site
☐ Cycle trail – direct access from site
☑ Cycle trail access within 2 km. of site
☐ Mountain bike track within 2 km. of site
☐ Bicycle hire on site
☐ Accompanied hiking trips
☐ Accompanied cycling trips
☐ Drying room for wet clothes/boots
☐ Packed lunch service

Facilities: Three heated sanitary blocks provide
a good supply of roomy shower cubicles,
washbasins, some washbasin/WC suites and
WCs. Facilities for babies and disabled visitors.
Well equipped laundry room. Good kitchen
with cookers, microwaves and dishwasher (free),
and sinks. Hot water is free. Gas supplies.
Motorcaravan services. Shop (1/5-30/8). Pizzeria,
licensed restaurant and café (all 1/5-30/8). Bar
(1/7-31/7). Outdoor heated swimming pool
(15/5-22/8). Playgrounds. Bouncy castle.
Boules. Canoe hire. Bicycle hire. Minigolf.
Family entertainment and activities. Football.
Off site: Golf 500 m. Riding 2 km. Fishing 4km.

Open: 12 April - 30 September.

Directions: Cross Öland road bridge from
Kalmar on road no. 137. Take exit for Öland
Djurpark/Saxnäs, then follow campsite signs.
Site is just north of the end of the bridge.
GPS: 56.68727, 16.48182

Charges guide

Per unit incl. electricity	SEK 175 - 430

Svegs Camping

Kyrkogränd 1, S-842 32 Sveg (Jämtlands Län)
t: 068 013 025   e: info@svegscamping.se
alanrogers.com/SW2845   www.camping.se/z32

Accommodation: ☑Pitch ☑Mobile home/chalet ☐ Hotel/B&B ☐ Apartment

On the 'Inlandsvägen' route through Sweden, the town centre is only a short walk from this neat, friendly site. Two supermarkets, a café and tourist information office are adjacent. The 80 pitches are in rows, on level grass, divided into bays by tall hedges, and with electricity (10/16A) available to 70. The site has boats, canoes and bicycles for hire, and the river frontage has a barbecue area with covered seating and fishing platforms. Alongside the river with its fountain, and running through the site is a pleasant well lit riverside walk. Places to visit include the town with its lovely church and adjacent gardens, some interesting old churches in the surrounding villages, and 16th-Century Remsgården, 14 km. to the west.

You might like to know

This is big country with miles of tracks to explore – the site owners will be pleased to recommend ideas.

- ☑ Walking notes or maps available
- ☐ Waymarked footpath – direct access from site
- ☑ Waymarked footpath within 1 km. of site
- ☐ Cycle trail – direct access from site
- ☑ Cycle trail access within 2 km. of site
- ☐ Mountain bike track within 2 km. of site
- ☐ Bicycle hire on site
- ☐ Accompanied hiking trips
- ☐ Accompanied cycling trips
- ☐ Drying room for wet clothes/boots
- ☐ Packed lunch service

Facilities: In the older style, sanitary facilities are functional rather than luxurious, providing stainless steel washing troughs, controllable hot showers with communal changing areas, and a unit for disabled visitors. Although a little short on numbers, facilities will probably suffice at most times as the site is rarely full. Kitchen and dining room with TV, four full cookers and sinks. Laundry facilities. TV room. Minigolf. Canoe, boat and bicycle hire. Fishing.

Open: All year.

Directions: Site is off road 45 behind the tourist information office in Sveg. Site is signed.
GPS: 62.03367, 14.37250

Charges guide

Per pitch	SEK 150
electricity	SEK 25

FINLAND – Ruovesi

Camping Haapasaaren Lomakylä

Haapasaarentie 5, FIN-34600 Ruovesi (Häme)
t: 044 080 0290   e: lomakyla@haapasaari.fi
alanrogers.com/FI2840   www.haapasaari.fi

Accommodation: ☑Pitch ☑Mobile home/chalet ☑Hotel/B&B ☐ Apartment

Haapasaaren is located on Lake Näsijärvi, around 70 km. north of Tampere in south western Finland. This is a well equipped site with a café and restaurant, a traditional Finnish outside dancing area and, of course, plenty of saunas! Rowing boats, canoes, cycles and, during the winter months, sleds are all available for rent. Fishing is very popular here. Pitches are grassy and of a good size. There is also a good range of accommodation to rent, including holiday cottages with saunas. The cosy restaurant has an attractive terrace and fine views across the lake. Alternatively, the site's café offers a range of snacks as well as Internet access. Haapasaaren's friendly owners organise a series of guided tours throughout the year. These include hiking and nature treks, berry and mushroom picking, and, during the winter, ice fishing and cross-country skiing. Helvetinjärvi National Park is one of the most dramatic areas of western Finland, and is made up of deep gorges and dense forests. There is a rich population of birds and occasionally even brown bears and lynx can be seen here.

Facilities: Café. Restaurant. Direct lake access. Saunas. Fishing. Minigolf. Boat and canoe hire. Bicycle hire. Guided tours. Play area. Tourist information. Chalets for rent. Off site: Walking and cycle routes. Boat trips. Helvetinjärvi National Park.

Open: All year.

Directions: From Helsinki, head north on the E12 motorway to Tampere and then northeast on N63-9 to Orivesi. Then, continue north on route 66 to Ruovesi and follow signs to the site. GPS: 61.99413, 24.069843

Charges guide

Per unit incl. 2 persons and electricity	€ 30,00
extra person	€ 4,50
child (under 15 yrs)	€ 2,00

You might like to know
After a vigorous day's hiking, try one of the site's traditional Finnish saunas, followed by a bracing swim in the adjacent lake.

☑ Walking notes or maps available
☐ Waymarked footpath – direct access from site
☑ Waymarked footpath within 1 km. of site
☐ Cycle trail – direct access from site
☑ Cycle trail access within 2 km. of site
☐ Mountain bike track within 2 km. of site
☑ Bicycle hire on site
☑ Accompanied hiking trips
☑ Accompanied cycling trips
☐ Drying room for wet clothes/boots
☐ Packed lunch service

FINLAND – Oulu

Nallikari Camping

Leiritie 10, FIN-90510 Oulu (Oulu)
t: 044 703 1353 e: nallikari.camping@ouka.fi
alanrogers.com/FI2970 www.nallikari.fi

Accommodation: ☑Pitch ☑Mobile home/chalet   ☐ Hotel/B&B ☐ Apartment

This is probably one of the best sites in Scandinavia, set in a recreational wooded area alongside a sandy beach on the banks of the Baltic Sea, with the added bonus of the adjacent Eden Spa complex. Nallikari provides 200 pitches, 176 with 16A electricity (seven also have water supply and drainage), plus an additional 78 cottages to rent, 28 of which are suitable for winter occupation. Oulu is a modern town, about 100 miles south of the Arctic Circle, that enjoys long, sunny and dry summer days. The Baltic, however, is frozen for many weeks in the winter and then the sun barely rises for two months. In early June the days are very long with the sun setting at about 23.30 and rising at 01.30! Nallikari, to the west of Oulu, is 3 km. along purpose-built cycle paths and the town has much to offer. Nordic walking, with or without roller blades, seems to be a recreational pastime for Finns of all ages! You might even be tempted to buy a pair of long, brightly-coloured walking sticks yourself! Oulu hosts events such as the Meri Oulu Festival in July and the Oulu Music Video Festival and forms the backdrop to the mind boggling, mime guitar playing world championships.

You might like to know

Bicycle hire is available on site including trailers for young children.

☑ Walking notes or maps available
☐ Waymarked footpath – direct access from site
☑ Waymarked footpath within 1 km. of site
☐ Cycle trail – direct access from site
☑ Cycle trail access within 2 km. of site
☐ Mountain bike track within 2 km. of site
☑ Bicycle hire on site
☐ Accompanied hiking trips
☐ Accompanied cycling trips
☐ Drying room for wet clothes/boots
☐ Packed lunch service

Facilities: The modern shower/WC blocks also provide male and female saunas, kitchen and launderette facilities. Facilities for disabled visitors. Motorcaravan service point. Playground. Reception with café/restaurant (June-Aug), souvenir and grocery shop. TV room. Free WiFi over site. Bicycle hire. Communal barbecues only. Off site: The adjacent Eden Centre provides excellent modern spa facilities where you can enjoy a day under the glass-roofed pool with its jacuzzis, saunas, Turkish baths and an Irish bath. Riding 2 km. Fishing 5 km. Golf 15 km.

Open: All year.

Directions: Leave road 4/E75 at junction with road 20 and head west down Kiertotie. Site well signed, Nallikari Eden, but continue on, just after traffic lights, cross a bridge and take the second on the right. Just before the Eden Centre turn right towards Leiritie and reception.
GPS: 65.02973, 25.41793

Charges guide

Per unit incl. 2 persons	€ 13,00 - € 26,00
extra person	€ 4,00
child (under 15 yrs)	€ 2,00
electricity	€ 4,50 - € 6,50

Camping Prahljust

An den Langen Brüchen 4, D-38678 Clausthal-Zellerfeld (Lower Saxony)
t: 053 231 300 e: camping@prahljust.de
alanrogers.com/DE3055 www.prahljust.de

Accommodation: ☑ Pitch ☐ Mobile home/chalet   ☐ Hotel/B&B   ☐ Apartment

In a woodland setting, 600 metres high and well away from main roads, Camping Prahljust is a quiet site providing plenty of fresh air in an attractive location. The site slopes gently down to a lake which is used for swimming, boating, windsurfing and fishing or in winter, ice skating. Of the 800 plus pitches, 500 are reserved for tourists. These are arranged in larger open, grass areas separated by hedges with plenty of tree cover and all have electrical connections. The Oberharz is a winter sports region and January and February are the busiest months, with cross-country skiing from the site. During the rest of the year this attractive region has much to offer; rambling, mountain-biking and rock climbing are all popular and the list of interesting places to visit is almost unending. Early mining activity brought wealth to the region resulting in the development of many beautiful medieval towns with their half-timbered houses and impressive public buildings. The reception has a good selection of brochures on display.

You might like to know

Why not hike up the Brocken, the most famous and highest (1142 m) mountain in the Harz? Alternatively, you can hike from the campsite along the 'Harzer Hexenstieg' (a new hiking trail across the Harz range).

- ☑ Walking notes or maps available
- ☑ Waymarked footpath – direct access from site
- ☐ Waymarked footpath within 1 km. of site
- ☐ Cycle trail – direct access from site
- ☑ Cycle trail access within 2 km. of site
- ☐ Mountain bike track within 2 km. of site
- ☐ Bicycle hire on site
- ☐ Accompanied hiking trips
- ☐ Accompanied cycling trips
- ☐ Drying room for wet clothes/boots
- ☐ Packed lunch service

Facilities: Three modern, heated toilet blocks are well maintained and hold all the usual facilities. Showers are free. Facilities for disabled visitors. Baby room. Washing machines, dryers, drying room and kitchen. Motorcaravan service point. Shop, restaurant and bar (closed Nov). Indoor, heated swimming pool (12x9 m; no shallow end). Sauna and solarium. Clubroom. Lake trail. Beer garden. Bicycle and kayak hire. There is also a small library with books (also in English) in reception. WiFi. Off site: Bus service 1 km. Riding 5 km. Downhill skiing 20 km.

Open: All year.

Directions: Leave Clausthal-Zellerfeld on the B242 towards Braunlage. After 1 km. site is signed. Turn south and site is a further 1 km. GPS: 51.78330, 10.38332

Charges guide

Per unit incl. 2 persons and electricity	€ 19,60 - € 22,10
extra person	€ 5,80 - € 6,30
child (2-14 yrs)	€ 3,50 - € 3,80
dog	€ 2,00

Winter charges higher.

Camping Goldene Meile

Simrockweg 9-13, D-53424 Remagen (Rhineland Palatinate)
t: 026 422 2222 e: info@camping-goldene-meile.de
alanrogers.com/DE3215 www.camping-goldene-meile.de/

Accommodation: ☑Pitch ☐ Mobile home/chalet ☐ Hotel/B&B ☐ Apartment

This site is on the banks of the Rhine between Bonn and Koblenz. Although there is an emphasis on permanent caravans, there are about 200 pitches for tourers (out of 500), most with 6A electricity and 100 with water and drainage. They are either in the central, more mature area or in a newer area where the numbered pitches of 80-100 sq.m. are arranged around an attractively landscaped, small fishing lake. Just five are by the busy river and there may be some noise from the trains that run on the other side. Access to the river bank is through a locked gate. Adjacent to the site is a large complex of open-air public swimming pools (campers pay the normal entrance fee). They claim always to find space for odd nights, except perhaps at Bank Holidays. This site is in a popular area and, although busy at weekends and in high season, appears to be well run.

You might like to know

The Rheinland Pfalz cycle trail extends for 330 km. and can be accessed directly from the site.

☑ Walking notes or maps available
☑ Waymarked footpath – direct access from site
☑ Waymarked footpath within 1 km. of site
☑ Cycle trail – direct access from site
☑ Cycle trail access within 2 km. of site
☑ Mountain bike track within 2 km. of site
☑ Bicycle hire on site
☐ Accompanied hiking trips
☐ Accompanied cycling trips
☐ Drying room for wet clothes/boots
☑ Packed lunch service

Facilities: The main toilet block is heated and clean, with some washbasins in cabins, showers and facilities for wheelchair users. A smaller block serves the newer pitches (no showers). Laundry and cooking facilities. Motorcaravan services. Gas. Shop, bar, restaurant and takeaway (all 1/4-30/10 and some weekends). Play areas. Entertainment for children (July/Aug). Bicycle hire. Main gate locked at 22.00 (also 13.00-15.00). Off site: Swimming pool complex adjacent (May-Sept). Riding 1 km. Cycling and walking in the Ahr valley. Remagen, Bonn and Cologne to visit. Boat trips on the Rhine and Mosel.

Open: All year.

Directions: Remagen is 20 km. south-southeast of Bonn. Site is beside the Rhine and is signed on the N9 road just south of Remagen. GPS: 50.57428, 7.25189

Charges guide

Per unit incl. 2 persons and electricity	€ 22,80 - € 24,40
extra person	€ 6,00
child (6-16 yrs)	€ 5,00
dog	€ 1,70

No credit cards.

GERMANY – Pfalzfeld

Country Camping Schinderhannes

D-56291 Hausbay-Pfalzfeld (Rhineland Palatinate)
t: 06746 80280 e: info@countrycamping.de
alanrogers.com/DE3242 www.countrycamping.de

Accommodation: ☑Pitch ☐ Mobile home/chalet ☐ Hotel/B&B ☐ Apartment

About 30 km. south of Koblenz, between Rhine and Mosel, this site is set in a 'bowl' of land which catches the sun all day. With trees and parkland all around, it is a peaceful and picturesque setting. There are 150 permanent caravans in a separate area from 90 short stay touring pitches on hardstanding. For longer stays, an area around the lake has a further 160 numbered pitches. These are of over 100 sq.m. on grass, some with hardstanding and all with 8A electricity. You can position yourself for shade or sun. The lake is used for swimming, inflatable boats and fishing. Some breeds of dog not admitted. English is spoken by the helpful reception staff. Country Camping could be a useful transit stop en-route to the Black Forest, Bavaria, Austria and Switzerland, as well as a family holiday. High in the Hunsrück (a large area with forests, ideal for walking and cycling), Schinderhannes himself was a legendary Robin Hood-type character, whose activities were curtailed in Mainz, at the end of a rope.

You might like to know

The Schinderhannes Bike Path runs close to the campsite and is a 38 km. trail between Emmelshausen and Simmern, with some delightful countryside and picture postcard villages along the way.

☑ Walking notes or maps available
☐ Waymarked footpath – direct access from site
☑ Waymarked footpath within 1 km. of site
☐ Cycle trail – direct access from site
☑ Cycle trail access within 2 km. of site
☐ Mountain bike track within 2 km. of site
☐ Bicycle hire on site
☐ Accompanied hiking trips
☐ Accompanied cycling trips
☐ Drying room for wet clothes/boots
☐ Packed lunch service

Facilities: The sanitary buildings, which can be heated, are of a high standard with one section in the reception/shop building for the overnight pitches, and the remainder close to the longer stay places. Laundry. Bar. Restaurant with takeaway. TV area. Skittle alley. Shop (all amenities 1/3-31/10 and Xmas). Tennis. Fishing. Play area. Rallies welcome. Torches useful. WiFi in restaurant and reception areas. Off site: Boat trips on the Rhine and Mosel. Walking in the Hunsrück region. Cycle paths.

Open: All year.

Directions: Site is 28 km. south of Koblenz. From A61 Koblenz-Ludwigshafen road, take exit 43 Pfalzfeld and on to Hausbay where site is signed. If using sat nav enter Hausbayer Strasse in Pfalzfeld. GPS: 50.10597, 7.56822

Charges guide

Per unit incl. 2 persons and electricity	€ 17,00 - € 23,00
extra person	€ 7,00
child (under 14 yrs)	€ 3,00
child (14 -17 yrs)	€ 5,00
dog	free - € 2,00

Camping & Ferienpark Teichmann

Zum Träumen 1A, D-34516 Vöhl-Herzhausen (Hessen)
t: 056 352 45 e: info@camping-teichmann.de
alanrogers.com/DE3280 www.camping-teichmann.de

Accommodation: ☑Pitch ☑Mobile home/chalet ☐ Hotel/B&B ☐ Apartment

Situated near the eastern end of the 27 km. long Edersee and the Kellerwald-Edersee National Park, this attractively set site is surrounded by wooded hills and encircles a six-hectare lake, which has separate areas for swimming, fishing and boating. Of the 500 pitches, 250 are for touring; all have 10A electricity and 50 have fresh and waste water connections. The pitches are on level grass, some having an area of hardstanding, and are separated by hedges and mature trees. At the opposite side of the lake from the entrance, there is a separate area for tents with its own sanitary block. The adjoining national park, a popular leisure attraction, offers a wealth of holiday/sporting activities including walking, cycling (there are two passenger ferries that take cycles), boat trips, cable car and much more. Full details are available at the friendly reception. For winter sports lovers, the ski centre at Winterberg is only 30 km. away from this all-year-round site. With a wide range of facilities for children, this is an ideal family site, as well as being suited to country lovers who can enjoy the endless forest and lakeside walks/cycle tracks in the park.

You might like to know

The new 'Urwaldsteig Edersee' route has been acclaimed as one of the region's most beautiful trails. It passes across steep slopes around the Edersee and along winding paths through some of the last remaining virgin forests of Germany.

- ☑ Walking notes or maps available
- ☐ Waymarked footpath – direct access from site
- ☑ Waymarked footpath within 1 km. of site
- ☐ Cycle trail – direct access from site
- ☑ Cycle trail access within 2 km. of site
- ☑ Mountain bike track within 2 km. of site
- ☑ Bicycle hire on site
- ☐ Accompanied hiking trips
- ☐ Accompanied cycling trips
- ☐ Drying room for wet clothes/boots
- ☐ Packed lunch service

Facilities: Three good quality sanitary blocks can be heated and have free showers, washbasins (open and in cabins), baby rooms and facilities for wheelchair users. Laundry. Motorcaravan services. Café and shop (both summer only). Restaurant by entrance open all day (closed Feb). Watersports. Boat and bicycle hire. Lake swimming. Fishing. Minigolf. Playground. Sauna. Solarium. Disco (high season). Internet access. Off site: New national park opposite site entrance. Riding 500 m. Golf 25 km. Cable car (bicycles accepted). Aquapark. Boat trips on the Edersee.

Open: All year.

Directions: Site is 45 km. southwest of Kassel. From A44 Oberhausen-Kassel autobahn, take exit 64 for Diemelstadt and head south for Korbach. Site is between Korbach and Frankenberg on the B252 road, 1 km. to the south of Herzhausen at the pedestrian traffic lights. GPS: 51.17550, 8.89067

Charges guide

Per unit incl. 2 persons and electricity	€ 26,00 - € 30,50
extra person	€ 5,90 - € 7,50
child (3-15 yrs)	€ 3,50 - € 4,40
dog	€ 3,60

Terrassen-Camping Alte Sägemühle

Badstrasse 57, D-79295 Sulzburg (Baden-Württemberg)
t: 076 345 51181   e: info@camping-alte-saegemuehle.de
alanrogers.com/DE3452   www.camping-alte-saegemuehle.de

Accommodation: ☑Pitch ☐ Mobile home/chalet   ☐ Hotel/B&B ☐ Apartment

This site lies just beyond the beautiful old town of Sulzburg with its narrow streets, and is on a peaceful road leading only to a natural swimming pool (formerly the mill pond) and a small hotel. It is set in a tree-covered valley with a stream running through the centre and is divided into terraced areas, each enclosed by high hedges and trees. Electrical connections (16A) are available on 42 of the 45 large touring pitches (long leads may be necessary). The site has been kept as natural as possible and is perfect for those seeking peace and quiet. The main building by the entrance houses reception, a small shop (which stocks a good selection of local wines) and the sanitary facilities. Run by the Geuss family (Frau Geuss speaks reasonable English) the site has won an award from the state for having been kept natural, for example, no tarmac roads, no minigolf, no playgrounds, etc. There are opportunities for walking straight from the site into the forest, and many walks and cycle rides are shown on maps available at reception. The tiny 500-year-old Jewish Cemetery reached through the site has an interesting history.

You might like to know

The Markgräflerland is widely considered to be one of the best hiking and cycling options in the Black Forest.

☑ Walking notes or maps available
☐ Waymarked footpath – direct access from site
☑ Waymarked footpath within 1 km. of site
☐ Cycle trail – direct access from site
☑ Cycle trail access within 2 km. of site
☐ Mountain bike track within 2 km. of site
☐ Bicycle hire on site
☐ Accompanied hiking trips
☐ Accompanied cycling trips
☐ Drying room for wet clothes/boots
☐ Packed lunch service

Facilities: In the main building, facilities are of good quality with two private cabins, separate toilets, dishwashing, washing machine and dryer. Small shop for basics, beer and local wines (all year). Torch may be useful. New room for tent guests and motorcaravan service point. Free bus and train travel in the Black Forest for guests. Off site: Natural, unheated swimming pool adjacent (June-Aug) with discount to campers. Public transport, bicycle hire, restaurants and other shops in Sulzburg 1.5 km. Riding 3 km. Fishing 8 km. Golf 12 km. Europa Park is less than an hour away.

Open: All year.

Directions: Site is easily reached from autobahn A5/E35. Take exit 64 for Bad Krozingen, south of Freiburg, onto B3 south to Heitersheim, then through Sulzburg, or if coming from south, exit 65 through Müllheim, Heitersheim and Sulzburg. Reception is to left of road. Note: arch in Sulzburg has only 3.1 m. height clearance. GPS: 47.83548, 7.72337

Charges guide

Per unit incl. 2 persons and electricity (plus meter)	€ 18,50 - € 21,00
extra person	€ 6,50
child (1-15 yrs)	€ 3,00

GERMANY – Neuenburg am Rhein

Gugel's Dreiländer Camping

Oberer Wald 3, D-79395 Neuenburg am Rhein (Baden-Württemberg)

t: **076 317 719**   e: **info@camping-gugel.de**

alanrogers.com/DE3455   www.camping-gugel.de

Accommodation: ☑Pitch ☐ Mobile home/chalet ☐ Hotel/B&B ☐ Apartment

Set in natural heath and woodland, Gugel's is an attractive site with 220 touring pitches, either in small clearings in the trees, in open areas or on a hardstanding section used for overnight stays. All have electricity (16A), and some also have water, waste water and satellite TV connections. Opposite is a meadow where late arrivals and early departures may spend the night. There may be some road noise near the entrance. The site may become very busy in high season and on bank holidays but you should always find room. The excellent pool and wellness complex add to the attraction of this all year site. There is a social room with satellite TV where guests are welcomed with a glass of wine and a slide presentation of the attractions of the area. The Rhine is within walking distance. Neuenburg is ideally placed not only for enjoying and exploring the south of the Black Forest, but also for night stops when travelling from Frankfurt to Basel on the A5 autobahn. The permanent caravans, set away from the tourist area with their well tended gardens, enhance rather than detract from the natural beauty.

You might like to know

The site is the starting point of a well signposted Nordic Walking course. You can borrow sticks and take part in an introduction to Nordic Walking.

- ☑ Walking notes or maps available
- ☑ Waymarked footpath – direct access from site
- ☐ Waymarked footpath within 1 km. of site
- ☐ Cycle trail – direct access from site
- ☑ Cycle trail access within 2 km. of site
- ☐ Mountain bike track within 2 km. of site
- ☐ Bicycle hire on site
- ☐ Accompanied hiking trips
- ☐ Accompanied cycling trips
- ☐ Drying room for wet clothes/boots
- ☐ Packed lunch service

Facilities: Three good quality, heated sanitary blocks include some washbasins in cabins. Baby room. Facilities for disabled visitors. Laundry facilities. Motorcaravan services. Shop. Excellent restaurant. Takeaway (weekends and daily in high season). Wellness centre. Indoor/outdoor pool. Boules. Tennis. Fishing. Minigolf. Barbecue. Beach bar. Bicycle hire. Community room with TV. Activity programme (high season). Play areas. Off site: Riding 1.5 km. Golf 5 km. Neuenburg, Breisach, Freiburg, Basel and the Black Forest.

Open: All year.

Directions: From autobahn A5 take Neuenburg exit, turn left, then almost immediately left at traffic lights, left at next junction and follow signs for 2 km. to site (called 'Neuenburg' on most signs). GPS: 47.79693, 7.55

Charges guide

Per unit incl. 2 persons and electricity	€ 26,50
extra person	€ 6,50
child (2-15 yrs)	€ 3,00
dog	€ 3,00

GERMANY – Krün-Obb

Alpen-Caravanpark Tennsee

Am Tennsee 1, D-82494 Krün-Obb (Bavaria (S))
t: 088 251 70 e: info@camping-tennsee.de
alanrogers.com/DE3680 www.camping-tennsee.de

Accommodation: ☑Pitch ☐ Mobile home/chalet ☐ Hotel/B&B ☑ Apartment

Tennsee is an excellent, friendly site in truly beautiful surroundings high up (1,000 m) in the Karwendel Alps with super mountain views, and close to many famous places of which Innsbruck (44 km) and Oberammergau (26 km) are two. Mountain walks are plentiful, with several lifts close by. It is an attractive site with good facilities including 164 serviced pitches with individual connections for electricity (up to 16A and two connections), gas, TV, radio, telephone, water and waste water. The other 80 pitches all have electricity and some of these are available for overnight guests at a reduced rate. Reception and comfortable restaurants, a bar, cellar youth room and a well stocked shop are all housed in attractive buildings. Many activities and excursions are organised to local attractions by the Zick family, who run the site in a very friendly, helpful and efficient manner.

You might like to know
This is great walking country. A family member leads accompanied hikes to view the Soiernseen or the spring flowers at Buckelwiesen.

☑ Walking notes or maps available
☐ Waymarked footpath – direct access from site
☑ Waymarked footpath within 1 km. of site
☐ Cycle trail – direct access from site
☑ Cycle trail access within 2 km. of site
☐ Mountain bike track within 2 km. of site
☑ Bicycle hire on site
☑ Accompanied hiking trips
☐ Accompanied cycling trips
☐ Drying room for wet clothes/boots
☐ Packed lunch service

Facilities: The first class toilet block has underfloor heating, washbasins in cabins and private units with WC, shower, basin and bidet for rent. Unit for disabled guests with the latest facilities. Baby bath, dog bathroom and a heated room for ski equipment (with lockers). Washing machines, free dryers and irons. Gas supplies. Motorcaravan services. Cooking facilities. Shop. Restaurants (waiter, self-service and takeaway). Bar. Youth room. Solarium. Bicycle hire. Playground. WiFi (charged). Organised activities and excursions. Bus service to ski slopes in winter. Off site: Fishing 400 m. Riding and golf 3 km. Discounted entry at Alpspitz-Wellenbad in Garmisch-Partenkirchen and Karwendel Bad in Mittenwald.

Open: All year excl. 6 November - 15 December.

Directions: Site is just off main Garmisch-Partenkirchen-Innsbruck road no. 2 between Klais and Krün, 15 km. from Garmisch watch for small sign Tennsee & Barmsee and turn right there for site. GPS: 47.49066, 11.25396

Charges guide

Per unit incl. 2 persons	€ 23,00 - € 26,00
extra person	€ 7,50 - € 8,00
child (6-16 yrs)	€ 3,00 - € 4,00
electricity per kWh	€ 0,70

Camping & Freizeitpark LuxOase

Arnsdorfer Strasse 1, Kleinröhrsdorf, D-01900 Dresden (Saxony)
t: 035 952 56666 e: info@luxoase.de
alanrogers.com/DE3833 www.luxoase.de

Accommodation: ☑Pitch ☐ Mobile home/chalet ☐ Hotel/B&B ☑ Apartment

This is a well organised and quiet site located just north of Dresden with easy access from the autobahn. The site has very good facilities and is arranged on grassland beside a lake. There is access from the site to the lake through a gate. Although the site is fairly open, trees do provide shade in some areas. There are 198 large touring pitches (plus 40 seasonal in a separate area), marked by bushes or posts on generally flat or slightly sloping grass. All have 10/16A electricity and 132 have water and drainage. At the entrance is an area of hardstanding (with electricity) for late arrivals. A brand new building provides excellent sanitary facilities, a separate washing area for children with showers in a castle and washbasins in a steam river boat. A wellness centre with pool and saunas, massages, fitness room, indoor playground for children and a hall for events for up to 200 people. You may swim, fish or use inflatables in the lake. There are many interesting places to visit apart from Dresden and Meissen, with the fascinating National Park Sächsische Schweiz (Saxon Switzerland) on the border with the Czech Republic offering some spectacular scenery. A member of Leading Campings group.

You might like to know
The site is well located to discover by bicycle, such attractions as the Baroque castle in Rammenau, the fortress at Stolpen, the gingerbread city of Pulsnitz, the beer-city Radeberg and the 'planetary' cycle track towards Radeberg.

- ☑ Walking notes or maps available
- ☐ Waymarked footpath – direct access from site
- ☑ Waymarked footpath within 1 km. of site
- ☐ Cycle trail – direct access from site
- ☑ Cycle trail access within 2 km. of site
- ☐ Mountain bike track within 2 km. of site
- ☐ Bicycle hire on site
- ☐ Accompanied hiking trips
- ☐ Accompanied cycling trips
- ☐ Drying room for wet clothes/boots
- ☐ Packed lunch service

Facilities: Two excellent buildings provide modern, heated facilities with private cabins, a family room, baby room, units for disabled visitors and eight bathrooms for hire. Jacuzzi. Kitchen. Gas. Motorcaravan services. Shop and bar (1/3-31/12) plus restaurant (15/3-31/12). Bicycle hire. Lake swimming. Sports field. Fishing. Play area. Sauna. Train, bus and theatre tickets from reception. Internet point. WiFi throughout (charged). Entertainment for children in high season. Minigolf. Fitness room. Regular guided bus trips to Dresden, Prague etc. Off site: Riding next door (lessons available). Golf 7.5 km.

Open: All year excl. February.

Directions: Site is 17 km. northeast of Dresden. From the A4 (Dresden-Görlitz) take exit 85 (Pulnitz) and travel south towards Radeberg. Pass through Leppersdorf and site is signed to the left. Follow signs for Kleinröhrsdorf and camping. Site is 4 km. from the autobahn exit. GPS: 51.120401, 13.980103

Charges guide

Per unit incl. 2 persons and electricity	€ 19,90 - € 26,60
extra person	€ 5,00 - € 8,00
child (3-15 yrs acc. to age)	€ 2,50 - € 4,50
dog	€ 2,50 - € 3,50

Camping Aktief

CZ-54982 Vernerovice (Kralovehradecky)
t: 491 582 138   e: bert.mien@tiscali.cz
alanrogers.com/CZ4555 www.aktief.cz

Accommodation: ☑ Pitch ☑ Mobile home/chalet ☐ Hotel/B&B ☑ Apartment

Camping Aktief is a small, rural site on the outskirts of the village of Vernerovice. The site is located close to the Polish border, east of the Krkonose (Giant) Mountains. The spectacular rock formations of Adrspach and Teplice nad Metuji are close at hand. This is a small site with just 20 pitches (all with 6A electricity), located in a tranquil and protected area with many fruit trees. From the campsite there are fine views around the surrounding rolling meadows and hills. The friendly Dutch owners have developed Camping Aktief as an important hiking centre. Plenty of other activities are also organised here, and detailed walking and cycle routes are available (in Dutch). The owners, Bert and Mien van Kampen, are happy to share their knowledge of the local area, including a number of good restaurants. They also organise special tours, including visits to a local brewery and glassworks. Bikes, mountain bikes and fishing equipment are available for hire on site. In peak season, a weekly barbecue is organised.

Facilities: Modern toilet block with underfloor heating. Sauna. Mobile home for rent (max 6 people). Accommodation in luxuriously converted farm buildings. Off site: Bus stop 200 m. Railway station 2 km. Hiking and cycle trails. Fishing.

Open: 15 April - 31 October.

Directions: Vernerovice is located in the northeast of the country, just 1 km from the Polish border. From route 302 between Broumov and Mieroszow (Poland) take the exit at Mezimisti and, in Vernerovice, follow signs to the campsite. GPS: 50.616409, 16.228651

Charges guide

Per unit incl 2 persons and electricity	€ 15,00

You might like to know

Eight-day hiking tour 'Pad door het Verloren Land' (Crossing the Lost Country) starting from the site, includes breakfast, luggage transports, overnight stays in the Czech Republic and Poland; bookings all year. Several MTB competitions in the summer season in the Adrspach-Teplice rock park.

☑ Walking notes or maps available
☑ Waymarked footpath – direct access from site
☑ Waymarked footpath within 1 km. of site
☑ Cycle trail – direct access from site
☑ Cycle trail access within 2 km. of site
☑ Mountain bike track within 2 km. of site
☑ Bicycle hire on site
☑ Accompanied hiking trips
☐ Accompanied cycling trips
☑ Drying room for wet clothes/boots
☐ Packed lunch service

Camping Frymburk

Frymburk 184, CZ-38279 Frymburk (Jihocesky)
t: **380 735 284** e: info@campingfrymburk.cz
alanrogers.com/CZ4720 www.campingfrymburk.cz

Accommodation: ☑Pitch ☑Mobile home/chalet ☐ Hotel/B&B ☐ Apartment

Camping Frymburk is beautifully located on the Lipno lake in southern Bohemia and is an ideal site. From this site, activities could include walking, cycling, swimming, sailing, canoeing or rowing and afterwards you could relax in the small, cosy bar/restaurant. You could enjoy a real Czech meal in one of the restaurants in Frymburk or on site. The site has 170 level pitches on terraces (all with 6A electricity, some with hardstanding and four have private sanitary units) and from the lower terraces on the edge of the lake there are lovely views over the water to the woods on the opposite side. A ferry crosses the lake from Frymburk where one can walk or cycle in the woods. The Dutch owner, Mr Wilzing, will welcome the whole family, personally siting your caravan. Children will be entertained by 'Kidstown' and the site has a small beach.

You might like to know

The cycle track from Frymburk to Lipno runs next to the site. It offers wonderful views of the lake and Frymburk, as well as a number of picnic spots.

☑ Walking notes or maps available
☐ Waymarked footpath – direct access from site
☑ Waymarked footpath within 1 km. of site
☑ Cycle trail – direct access from site
☐ Cycle trail access within 2 km. of site
☐ Mountain bike track within 2 km. of site
☑ Bicycle hire on site
☐ Accompanied hiking trips
☐ Accompanied cycling trips
☐ Drying room for wet clothes/boots
☐ Packed lunch service

Facilities: Three immaculate toilet blocks with washbasins, preset showers (charged) and an en-suite bathroom with toilet, basin and shower. Facilities for disabled visitors. Launderette. Restaurant and bar (10/5-15/9). Motorcaravan services. Playground. Canoe, bicycle, pedalos, rowing boat and surfboard hire. Kidstown. Volleyball competitions. Rafting. Bus trips to Prague. Torches useful. Internet access and WiFi. Off site: Shops and restaurants in the village 900 m. from reception. Golf 7 km. Riding 20 km.

Open: 29 April - 1 October.

Directions: Take exit 114 at Passau in Germany (near Austrian border) towards Freyung in Czech Republic. Continue to Philipsreut, from there follow the no. 4 road towards Vimperk. Turn right a few kilometres after border towards Volary on no. 141 road. From Volary follow the no. 163 road to Horni Plana, Cerna and Frymburk. Site is on 163 road, right after village.
GPS: 48.655947, 14.170239

Charges guide

Per unit incl. 2 persons and electricity	CZK 460 - 810
extra person	CZK 80 - 130
child (under 12 yrs)	CZK 60 - 90

No credit cards.

CZECH REPUBLIC – Nové Straseci

Camping Bucek

Tratice 170, CZ-27101 Nové Straseci (Stredocesky)
t: 313 564 212 e: info@campingbucek.cz
alanrogers.com/CZ4825 www.campingbucek.cz

Accommodation: ☑Pitch ☑Mobile home/chalet ☐ Hotel/B&B ☑ Apartment

Camping Bucek is a pleasant, Dutch-owned site 30 km. west of Prague. Its proprietors also own Camping Frymburk (CZ4720). Bucek is located on the edge of woodland and has direct access to a small lake with a private beach. Here you can enjoy canoes and rowing boats which are available to guests free of charge. There are 100 pitches here, many with pleasant views over the lake, and all with electrical connections (6A). Four pitches have their own private sanitary facilities. Shade is quite limited. On-site amenities include an indoor swimming pool, play equipment, trampolines and there is also an animation programme. A short distance from the site is a railway station from which you can catch a fast train into the centre of Prague. The castles of Karlstejn and Krivoklát are also within easy reach, along with Karlovy Vary.

You might like to know
The site is 5 km. from the small town of Nové Strašecí, with all services available there.

☑ Walking notes or maps available
☐ Waymarked footpath – direct access from site
☑ Waymarked footpath within 1 km. of site
☐ Cycle trail – direct access from site
☑ Cycle trail access within 2 km. of site
☐ Mountain bike track within 2 km. of site
☐ Bicycle hire on site
☐ Accompanied hiking trips
☐ Accompanied cycling trips
☐ Drying room for wet clothes/boots
☐ Packed lunch service

Facilities: Renovated toilet blocks with free hot showers. Washing and drying machine. Restaurant and bar. Direct lake access with pedaloes and canoes. Indoor swimming pool with paddling pool. Minigolf. Play area. Trampolines. Activity programme. Walking and cycling opportunities. WiFi throughout. Off site: Revnicov 2 km. with shops (including a supermarket), bars and restaurants. Fishing 3 km. Riding 4 km. Karlovy Vary 10 km. Prague 40 km. Koneprusy caves.

Open: 24 April - 15 September.

Directions: From the west, take no. 6/E48 express road towards Prague. Site is close to this road, 3 km. after the Revnicov exit and is clearly signed from this point. Coming from the east, ignore other camping signs and continue until Bucek is signed (to the north).
GPS: 50.1728, 13.8348

Charges guide

Per unit incl. 2 persons and electricity	CZK 450 - 670
extra person	CZK 75 - 100
child (under 12 yrs)	CZK 50 - 75
dog	CZK 50 - 60

No credit cards.

Autocamping Stara Hora

Oravska Priehrada, SK-02901 Namestovo (Zilina)
t: 043 552 2223 e: camp.s.hora@stonline.sk
alanrogers.com/SK4905 www.oravskapriehrada.sk

Accommodation: ☑Pitch ☑Mobile home/chalet ☐ Hotel/B&B ☐ Apartment

Stara Hora has a beautiful location on the Orava artificial lake. It is in the northeast of Slovakia in the Tatra Mountains and attracts visitors from all over Europe which creates a happy and sometimes noisy atmosphere. The site has its own pebble beach with a large grass area behind it for sunbathing. Autocamping Stara Hora is on steeply sloping ground with 160 grassy pitches, all for touring units and with 10A electricity. The lower pitches are level and have good views over the lake, pitches at the top are mainly used by tents. The lake provides opportunities for fishing, boating and sailing and the area is good for hiking and cycling and in winter, it is a popular skiing area.

You might like to know

There are some wonderful walks around the lake – the site managers will be pleased to recommend popular routes.

☑ Walking notes or maps available
☐ Waymarked footpath – direct access from site
☑ Waymarked footpath within 1 km. of site
☐ Cycle trail – direct access from site
☑ Cycle trail access within 2 km. of site
☐ Mountain bike track within 2 km. of site
☐ Bicycle hire on site
☐ Accompanied hiking trips
☐ Accompanied cycling trips
☐ Drying room for wet clothes/boots
☐ Packed lunch service

Facilities: The modern toilet block has British style toilets, open washbasins and controllable hot showers (free). It could be pressed in high season and hot water to the showers is only available 07.00-10.00 and 19.00-22.00. Shop for basics. Bar and lakeside bar. Small restaurant. Basic playground (new playground planned). Pedalo, canoe and rowing boat hire. Water-skiing. Fishing (with permit). Torch useful. Off site: Slanica Island.

Open: May - September.

Directions: From Ruzomberok take E77 road north towards Trstena. Turn left in Tvrdosin on the 520 road towards Námestovo. Site is on the right. GPS: 49.359333, 19.555

Charges guide

Per person	€ 2,42
child	€ 1,21
pitch incl. car	€ 3,04
electricity	€ 2,73

SLOVAKIA – Martin

Autocamping Turiec

Kolonia hviezda 92, SK-03608 Martin (Zilina)
t: **043 428 4215** e: **recepcia@autocampingturiec.sk**
alanrogers.com/SK4910 www.autocampingturiec.sk

Accommodation: ☑Pitch ☑Mobile home/chalet ☐ Hotel/B&B ☐ Apartment

Turiec is situated in northeast Slovakia, 1.5 kilometres from the small village of Vrutky, four kilometres north of Martin, at the foot of the Lucanska Mala Fatra mountains and with castles nearby. This good site has views towards the mountains and is quiet and well maintained. Holiday activities include hiking in summer, skiing in winter, both downhill and cross-country. There is room for about 30 units on slightly sloping grass inside a circular tarmac road with some shade from tall trees. Electrical connections (6A) are available for all places. You will receive a friendly welcome from Viktor Matovcik and his wife Lydia. A wooden chalet by the side of the camping area has a TV rest room and a small games room. Down the hill is a splendid restaurant serving excellent food. English is spoken.

You might like to know

Turiec is located in a heavily wooded area at the foothills of the Martinské mountains, with miles of excellent walks close at hand.

☑ Walking notes or maps available
☐ Waymarked footpath – direct access from site
☑ Waymarked footpath within 1 km. of site
☐ Cycle trail – direct access from site
☑ Cycle trail access within 2 km. of site
☐ Mountain bike track within 2 km. of site
☐ Bicycle hire on site
☐ Accompanied hiking trips
☐ Accompanied cycling trips
☐ Drying room for wet clothes/boots
☐ Packed lunch service

Facilities: One acceptable sanitary block to the side of the camping area, but in winter the facilities in the bungalow at the entrance are used. Cooking facilities. Badminton. Rest room with TV. Small games room. Covered barbecue. WiFi. Off site: Shop outside entrance. Swimming pool 1.5 km.

Open: All year.

Directions: Site is signed from E18 road (Zilina-Martin) in the village of Vrutky, 3 km. northwest of Martin. Turn south on the bend and follow signs to Martinské Hole. GPS: 49.108492, 18.899467

Charges guide

Per unit incl. 2 persons	
and electricity	€ 15,20 - € 17,60
extra person	€ 4,30
child (6-10 yrs)	€ 2,60
dog	€ 0,70 - € 1,30

Been to any good campsites lately?
We have

You'll find them here...

The UK's market leading independent guides to the best campsites

... also here...

101 great campsites, ideal for your specific hobby,
pastime or passion

Want independent campsite reviews at your fingertips?

You'll find them here...

Over 3,000 in-depth campsite reviews at **www.alanrogers.com**

alan rogers

...and even here...

FREE Alan Rogers bookstore app
- digital editions of all 2013 guides
alanrogers.com/digital

An exciting free app from iTunes
the Apple app store or the
Android Market

Want to book your holiday on one of Europe's top campsites?

We can do it for you. No problem.

The best campsites in the most popular regions - we'll take care of everything

alan rogers ⬤ travel

alan
rogers

Discover the best campsites in Europe
with Alan Rogers

alanrogers.com
01580 214000

index

index

index